On the
Clarion Experiment:

"Traditionally, the magazines have been the only place to train new science fiction writers; we now know there can be other ways. [One] is to hold workshops like the Clarion Workshop in Fantasy and Science Fiction. . . . This volume contains the work of 16 new science fiction writers. . . . There are some I am putting my money on."
—Damon Knight in *Charting Utopia*

"They bring to their craft a verve, a fire, a ferocity that is unhappily absent in all by a handful of the writers who have gone before them."
—Harlan Ellison in **Dreamers on a Barricade**

"A phenomenal percentage of writers from Clarion . . . have gone on to begin selling s-f stories and novels. . . . In this time, s-f has been approached from many new directions. The Clarion Workshop is one of the most exciting."
—Samuel R. Delany in *Reading Between the Words*

Other SIGNET Titles You Will Enjoy

CLARION

an anthology of speculative fiction and criticism from the Clarion Writers' Workshop

edited by

Robin Scott Wilson

A SIGNET BOOK from
NEW AMERICAN LIBRARY
TIMES MIRROR

Acknowledgments

"Just Dead Enough" by C. Davis Belcher was originally published under the title "The Price" in *Orbit 5* (G. P. Putnam's
Sons), copyright © 1969 by Damon Knight.

"Sending the Very Best" by Ed Bryant was originally published
in *New Worlds 197* (January 1970). Copyright © 1970, New
Worlds Publishing.

"Song from a Forgotten Hill" by Glen Cook is reprinted from
Worlds of Tomorrow. Copyright © 1971 by Worlds of Tomorrow.

"A Free Pass to the Carnival" by Geo. Alec Effinger was
originally published in *The Magazine of Fantasy and Science
Fiction*, May 1971. Copyright © 1971 by The Magazine of
Fantasy and Science Fiction.

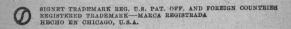
SIGNET, SIGNET CLASSICS, SIGNETTE, MENTOR AND PLUME BOOKS
are published by The New American Library, Inc.,
1301 Avenue of the Americas, New York, New York 10019

FIRST PRINTING, JUNE, 1971

PRINTED IN THE UNITED STATES OF AMERICA

We are pleased to announce the winners of the NAL prizes for the best stories from the 1970 Clarion Writers' Workshop. The stories marked by an asterisk appear in this anthology:

1st prize: * "Wheels" by Robert Thurston
2nd prize: "Spectra" by Vonda McIntyre
3rd prize: * "Silent Hands" by Gerard F. Conway and
              * "An Uneven Evening" by Steve Herbst

Honorable Mention:

    * "Just Dead Enough" by C. Davis Belcher
      "Childfinder" by Octavia Estelle Butler
    * "Song From a Forgotten Hill" by Glen Cook

    * "A Free Pass to the Carnival" by Geo. Alec Effinger

For DAVID A. HILTON

A memorial he would have enjoyed

CONTENTS

INTRODUCTION

In 1967, when I left the Central Intelligence Agency to join the faculty at Clarion State College as Professor of English, I was asked to establish a summer writing program. Since I did not know how to go about this, knew only that I wanted to teach writing as a craft, and had published a couple of dozen science-fiction stories (mostly under the name "Robin Scott"), I proposed with some hesitancy that I conduct a workshop in the writing of science fiction and fantasy, fully expecting some comment that science fiction was not, after all, very much respected in Academe.

But I underestimated the recent surge of academic interest in "speculative fiction," as I did the foresight of the Clarion administration. Both my Chairman, Dr. Lester D. Moody, and Liberal Arts Dean John Mellon greeted my proposal with enthusiasm and gave me a free hand in the organization of the first Clarion Writers' Workshop in Fantasy and Science Fiction. I went to the Milford Science Fiction Writers Conference—an annual meeting of professional writers directed by Damon Knight—to see how it was done.

I got much more than knowledge from Milford. After some initial skepticism, most of the writers there assembled gave me encouragement and ideas; it is to them that I owe my deepest gratitude for what Clarion became.

The Workshop was shaped in its first year by its staff of Visiting Lecturers: Judith Merril, Fritz Leiber, Harlan Ellison, Kate Wilhelm, and Damon Knight. In subsequent years, Frederik Pohl, Samuel R. Delany, Joanna Russ, and James Sallis brought new enthusiasm and their own unique brands of perception to our classroom.

And then the participants: the sixty-five Clarion Workshop alumni represent twenty states and range in age from seventeen to sixty-seven. Among them are a doctor, a musician, an artist, a magician, a computer programmer, a plant pathologist, a photographer, a journalist, and a saddlemaker; others are students and teachers and housewives. They are black, white, and Amerind; they all very much wanted to write. Twenty-seven of them have become selling authors; another dozen soon will be.

They all very much wanted to write . . . and that is why Clarion worked for so many. I did not want another summer writers' conference full of middle-aged ladies in tennis shoes waving dog-eared manuscripts at literary lions. I did not want lectures and formality and reading fees and the exploitation of vain aspirations. I wanted people who wanted to write, not people who wanted to be writers; I wanted a staff who would read manuscripts out of love and interest, not for a fee. I was fortunate enough to find such people, such a staff, and they all lived together in a wormy old dormitory and they played and they talked and they worked and they criticized and they wrote. And wrote. Each summer, about twenty people produced about four thousand pages of finished manuscript.

I think the Clarion experiment was successful, and I submit this book in evidence.

Winnetka, Illinois, 15 October 1970

A number of people and organizations contributed to the enrichment of the 1970 Clarion Workshop, and I wish to thank them as heartily as I can in this small space. Notable was the endowment by the New American Library of handsome prizes for Clarion writers. And special thanks go to George T. Delacorte, Edward L. Ferman, Ejler Jakobsson, Harlan Ellison, Robert Silverberg, Ray Fisher, and the thousands of good-hearted people at the 27th World Science Fiction Convention at St. Louis. Science Fiction is full of Friday's children. . . .

RSW

Something Happens

by Kate Wilhelm

We arrive at Clarion with no set theory, no teaching aids, no formal training in teaching writing, or anything else. The students have had each other for four weeks, have had other visiting lecturers, have had Robin, who does have the theory and training. We feel we are the innocents, the neophytes in this situation. Waiting for us is a stack of manuscripts. Some of them were brought from home, most of them were written at Clarion. Some of them are in the third version already, with the other two versions also in the stack and no way of telling by looking which came first. Twenty names, all free-floating until a day or two in class when the names settle down on the persons, and the manuscripts seem to adhere to their owners. After the first twenty-four hours you accept this as the way of life. Classes in the morning, reading and talking to the students afternoons and evenings.

The talk goes on most of the time. It doesn't matter where it starts, it comes back to writing. And you realize that probably for the first time for most of these kids they are being treated as peers by those hired to instruct them. And you also realize that successful teaching is a two-way exchange. After several days we begin to schedule individual conferences.

"Why did you put a spaceship in the middle of the town?"

"Nothing was happening. I wanted them to blow it all up."

"Why?"

"I hate it so much."

"*You* hate it. We all have someplace that we hate with that much intensity, and by bringing in the hand of God, so to speak, and letting him do the dirty work you deny us the opportunity of getting rid of that hated place." Silence. "Why does your protagonist hate it anyway?"

That breaks the silence. Half an hour later: "That's your story. When you started to talk about the town you started with little things, and they built and built. You haven't done anything to ease your feelings about it at all. Having a spaceship come down and wipe it all out won't relieve the anxiety you've aroused. Your protagonist has to be honest about his feelings, and has to be honest in dealing with them, somehow. He can blow the town up, or run away from it, or be conquered by it, but *he* has to deal with it. Not an eleventh-hour spaceship."

And with another student, another kind of story problem. "Saying it's horrible doesn't make it horrible. Rather it dilutes what I conceive of as being horrible. Read that sentence over without any adjectives at all. Now what else do we positively have to know about the castle?"

"I hate that kind of flat writing. I like to read flowery language."

"Flowery? As in a garden? Where each plant is selected for a particular effect? Or as in a weedy patch where seedlings have been allowed to crowd out the hybrids? That's what happens, unwanted and unnecessary words creep in and spoil the overall plan. Like here: 'ancient,' 'crumbling,' 'moldering,' 'ruined,' 'shadowy,' 'menacing,' and so on. You don't have to beat us over the head with it."

"Why did you circle words here and there?"

"They aren't the right words. It reminds me of an artist who reaches without looking for the colors he wants, and then settles for what he finds on his brush. Often the words are close, sometimes they hit, but quite often they are approximations. 'Flaunt' isn't 'flout.' A bell can peal, not a light."

Again and again the question of words as signs comes up. Symbols rise from the unconscious, quite unbidden; words are conscious attempts to evoke in the reader the same meaning that was in the mind of the writer. Too many descriptive words hide the story just as effectively as too many billboards hide the landscape. If the approach to writing can be classified at all, I would be tempted to dichotomize: those who start as storytellers, and those who start as wordsmiths, poets. The drive of the story pushes the storyteller into clumsy phrases, purple prose, redundancies, but he has a story complete with beginning, middle, end. Things happen and there is a resolution. The wordsmiths often have collages of beautiful sketched images, and little else.

"This is so well done that I'd like to see you finish it somehow. It isn't a story." And what is a story? I have to ask myself, and realize that there is no one answer. But I know it when I see it.

"How?"

Persevere. Persevere. "There has to be tension between the reader and the story, and through it to the writer. Not surface suspense, no chases or threats, nothing like that. But a recognition that your man is you, that he is me, that when you describe him thoroughly alone in a city of millions, you're really talking about every one of us. This story doesn't do that. He never seems to know that he is that alone and always will be."

"But I've felt exactly like that. Go home and close the door and go to bed because there's nothing else to do."

"Sure. But at some point in your life you made the discovery that that's how it was. That was the crucial point, the thing that's missing from the story. We have no way of knowing if your man has learned that, or if he ever will learn it. If it doesn't matter to him, the story dissolves into a bit of trivia, and we feel cheated because you have aroused our anxieties without defining them or resolving them in some way, even in the negative by saying, 'That's how it is folks, no use fighting it.' "

"And what about the story where nothing happens? The slice-of-life story?"

"There's no such story. If nothing happens on the page, it has to happen to the reader. But something happens, or there's no story. An intimate glimpse into the daily life of a person can satisfy in that it reveals not just the character, but also the author, his attitude toward life, other people, situations. Or perhaps it forces the reader to examine his own attitudes. But something happens. The words bridge the emptiness between the writer's unconscious and that of the reader."

Writing is addictive. At first it is very hard to find the time for it. Life is too demanding; family, friends, school, movies, whatever, they all get in the way and the weeks flow. An hour now and then, a story that you want to finish and sit up half the night to do, and finally after some time, you know that writing won't work like that. It's painful to be interrupted in the middle of something and find on returning that it no longer is alive. So you try to arrange a schedule, one hour every day, or two hours three days a week, anything that you can live with. And the times comes when if you use your writing hours for anything else you are edgy and unhappy. That's when you know you're hooked. For most people I suspect the primary reward of writing is writing. For a brief time you are in touch with your own unconscious, things you didn't know you knew appear on the paper, you become oblivious to the small nuisances that in the beginning were enough to stop you cold. A minor headache is forgotten. Tomorrow's worries fade out of sight. Yesterday's disappointments dim. And you're writing. After the first sacred draft is completed, then comes the real work. Successful writing is a happy combination of mixing conscious control with unconscious creation. Neither will produce good fiction. Sometimes you will see the unconscious trying awkwardly to disguise the product of its own outpourings.

"Just tell me what you want the story to mean?"

"Well, this man is a mediocre artist until he gets this statuette, and when he rubs it, occult powers flow into this time period and invade him and turn him into a really great artist . . ."

They know. These children who have never turned out a salable story, who are still smooth-cheeked, they know. Basically the story is about the possession of art, and the jealousy of the girl whose lover is so possessed. And there are occult powers and too many characters and evil spirits doing diabolical things. But underlying it all is the honest, very true story of the artist's struggle with those forces that would make him accept a life of normality, at the cost of his art. So you talk with the young writer, try to find out if he is ready to face the reality behind his fiction. Sometimes they aren't ready yet. One student, who had turned out juvenilia for five weeks, came up with a powerful story questioning the beliefs of his people— honest, true, real, lovely, poignant. When confronted with what he had, he withdrew it. It would hurt his parents too much. He didn't know the answers yet. Back to the juvenilia. In the present case the boy was so excited by the story that he finally uncovered after more than an hour of talking. At an early point in that time, he began doing the questioning, and the story as it evolved from the mass of wordage was his story. All there from the start, but buried under such a load of garbage that it never would have been found by anyone not actively searching for something.

Again and again we stress that: it is your story. What do you want it to do? What effect are you trying for? Story as entertainment? Therapy? Surrealist imagery? Communication? What do you want? I try not to influence anyone toward any particular school of writing. I do try to help them find out what they want to do. I want them to deal honestly with their materials.

Years ago in high school I wanted to become an organic chemist. The dean of women had me in for an hour-long interview and the message that I carried away was simply forget it. Unless you want to teach there's no future for women in science.

So I've been on that firing line for a long, long time. When I started to write I debated about what name to use. At that time there were far fewer women in the field of science fiction than there are today, but it didn't occur to me to use initials. I was debating about using my maiden name, Meredith, or Catherine or Kate. Actually, and only incidentally, my real name is Katie, but that would have been silly. I have four brothers, three sons, and a husband. I learned along about the time I was cutting my two-year molars that if you want to compete with males in any field you've got to be as good as, or preferably better than, they are. Or don't race.

So I see the initialed manuscripts and ask, "Why?"

"I want to be published."

"I get published. I could reel off the names of a dozen other women who get published, without hiding behind initials."

Silence.

"What I think when I see initials is that *they* have won. *They*'ve made you ashamed of being a woman." I'm certain it isn't so much what I say as what I am—a woman writer with husband and family, getting along—that lets them listen to me. They know what they face. "It won't be easy," I tell them. "The highest compliment any man can pay a woman writer is to say, 'Hey, you write as good as a man.' And your answer, which you should rehearse to achieve just the right shade of sweetness and bite, is: 'Oh, no, you're wrong. I write a damn sight better than most men.' If you're good, you'll succeed. And the sweetest success is the hardest to come by, forcing *them* to accept you and recognize your worth on *their* terms."

Invariably there are those who will want to tell you
their stories, or hand you the beginning and tell you the
rest, to get an opinion before they waste time writing it.
Frankly I can only say I don't know yet. A story has a
shape, balance, and rhythm, quite aside from its fictional
content. You can't assume these qualities until it is a
finished thing. Bad writing doesn't necessarily mean a bad
story, not from a new writer. If the basic soundness is
there, then it can be salvaged in spite of bad writing, sometimes. But more important, a piece of fiction has its own
energy. A short story has a burst of energy that is dis-
pelled in a relatively short time, usually, while a novel is
like a slow charge on a battery. It can be drained off just
as slowly without harm. Any generality about writing is
as valuable as generalities about anything else. Always
regard them with suspicion. However, that warning out of
the way, I go back to the position already stated. A writer
should not use up the story energy in telling it, discussing
it with other people. He should write it. I won't comment
on unfinished work unless it is a novel. And that's a whole
new game.

I give out personal assignments, too. After reading a
few stories from each of the students it is sometimes not
too difficult to see where the stumbling block lies. Write a
story about someone you really despise, but from a sym-
pathetic viewpoint. (People don't go around shooting each
other, you know. Think about your people a bit more.
Know them.) Or, write a story set in your own home
town, about places and people you know. (One *Star Trek*
story after another. Can he do anything else?) Or, write
a story that is plotted first. (His stories all tend to go
A . . . B . . . B$_1$ . . . B$_2$ . . . B$_3$ . . . Z. A beginning, something happening again and again and again, an end. No
real development.) Or, do a character study showing why
a man did something he knew would have unpleasant
consequences. (His stories are so full of fights and action
that you never know who hit whom or why for all the
dust.) Or, a quiet horror story. Or, a story about a man
from his viewpoint. (When told she could probably do con-
fession stories with the style she had slipped into, she was
furious. Can she change it?) And so on.

What I'm really saying over and over is: Care! Write
where you care. Write where it hurts, where you're puzzled,
or frightened, or joyous. All you have to give is yourself,
and if you hide too far behind your story, I won't be
touched by it. I won't read it.

Do we teach writing? I don't know. Something happens. Maybe just having things pointed out that all writers find out eventually telescopes the time it takes from that first purple epic to a published story. Maybe being accepted by writers as potential if not actual writers is enough to get them over the first hurdles. Maybe having lecturers who want them to succeed, who believe in them, does it. I don't know. Something happens.

Mel Gilden, a whimsical young Californian, describes the genesis of this story: "I had just finished seeing *Bob and Carol and Ted and Alice*. There is a scene in the movie where all the title characters are in bed together. I thought of the problems that we have with just two sexes, and I figured that the problems would increase geometrically with each added sex. This, in combination with an old piece of graffiti, made my story."

The graffito, for readers unobservant in washrooms, runs something like this:

First hand: "I like to screw grils."
Second hand: "You mean *girls*."
First hand: "Yeah, I mean *girls*."
Third hand: "But what about us grils?"

What About Us Grils?

by Mel Gilden

The cellar stank of a ghastly mixture of off-world brews. Lerd stood at the top of the stairs peering into the darkness. His eyes, already normally bulging, took on a kind of spherical symmetry. And then with the stiff three-legged stride the Droshii use when in a hurry, Lerd loped down the stairs and navigated his way between the scattered tables to the bar.

The dragon who was tending it that night said, "What'll you have?" His voice was a pleasant contralto.

"I'm looking for a grundy and a furble," Lerd whispered.

"What?" The dragon leaned over the bar, clanking his scales against the surrogate wood finish. His teeth glowed where they caught the sparse lighting.

Lerd turned away from the bad breath that came from the saber-lined mouth that hung a foot and a half above his head. Controlling his nausea, he took the dragon by the arm and led him to the end of the bar. The dragon began to pick his teeth with a taloned finger.

"Listen," Lerd said, "I'm looking for a grundy and a furble. I need them right now. Tonight. Do you know where I can find them?"

The dragon looked fiercely at Lerd. "What do you think this is, a whorehouse?" He beagn to walk away.

Lerd laid a five-credit note on the bar.

The dragon came back. He speared the money expertly with the nail of one finger and stuffed it somewhere under his scales. "You were saying?"

"I need a grundy and a furble tonight. Before I metamorphose into a grundy."

21

"Very interesting." The dragon held his hand over his mouth, elaborately being bored, as he tried to stifle a yawn.

"I already have a tibbit, but I don't know how long she'll last either."

"You *do* have a problem," the dragon said. "It's pretty difficult to find mates for Droshii here on Terra."

"You're telling me."

The dragon picked at his scales. He lifted one up and scratched at the tender skin underneath, letting it fall back with a metallic click.

Lerd put down another five-credit note.

The dragon disposed of the money as he had before. He said, "You see that fellow over in the corner?"

"The one with the fluorescent markings on his body?"

"That's him. He's a Pilto and one of the best procurers in Mid-district Los Angeles. He should be able to help you."

Lerd said, "Thank you." He walked to the Pilto on his three bony legs.

"Sir? The dragon said you could help me with a problem I have."

The Pilto looked up with its compound eyes. The luminescent triangles that covered its face all pointed toward the center of its head, striping its face like a bumblebee's body.

"What's that?" It sipped up some brown sludge with its hollow tongue.

"I desperately need a grundy and a furble."

"That's easy enough to do," it said. "I can arrange the meeting for tomorrow evening."

"But that will be too late. My tibbit and I will have changed by then."

"So? Can't you copulate at the next stage?"

"Of course. But I've never done it as a gril."

The Pilto shook his head. "Well, in that case . . ." He stopped and his lights blinked. "Just a minute." His eyes went milky.

Lerd watched in fascination as the Pilto wobbled his head and waved his insectlike arms. Then his eyes cleared again and he said to Lerd, "There is a chance." He scribbled something on a piece of paper. "There is someone there who can help you."

Lerd clutched the paper eagerly. "How much do I owe you?"

"Just pay Mr. Herbinger at this address. We work together."

The lobby was a cotton-candy nightmare. The walls, floors, and ceiling merged together without a break, making the hall an ellipsoid. It was covered with pink fluff.

Lerd stroked the soft fur that ran down the center of the tibbit's back. He said, "Now don't worry about a thing, Sava. I've been told that this Pilto is the best pimp in Mid-district Los Angeles."

"I trust you, Lerd. I really do."

They walked claw in claw across the great feathery sea that lay between them and a line of closed doors. The third one they came to had "Mr. Herbinger" written on it in gold letters.

Lerd knocked.

A cheerful voice said, "Come in," and the door slipped aside. They walked into the office. A man was standing behind a large mahogany desk.

"Ah, yes." Mr. Herbinger said. "The Pilto called and told me about your problem." He looked at Sava, who immediately blushed green. "And you must be the tibbit. How nice."

The man rubbed his hands together and sat down behind his desk. Two Droshii chairs grew from the floor like mushrooms.

"Can you really help us?" Lerd asked.

The man laughed. "Of course we can. Here at the Love and Universal Satisfaction Trust we've handled many cases that were much more difficult than yours. For example, the Red-Ringed Volcuna has eight sexes, each of which reaches sexual readiness in time with a different one of Rigel VII's moons. The Feathered Pu-Pu of Gamma Hydra VI, though they are asexual, need a member of their own race to break off their budding offspring or it will kill the parent. The most interesting of all, of course, is the Flonx from the Pleiades region. The Flonx not only needs a male and a female for copulation, but also a piece of ziml root. This root is useless for anything else, even to a Flonx. But without it, a love-starved Flonx will actually die of sexual deprivation."

Lerd said, "And you've helped all of them?"

"Yes, we have; so you see, your problem is really no problem at all."

Lerd looked longingly at Sava. "Then you have a grundy and a furble?" He sounded relieved.

Mr. Herbinger stopped looking benignly at the space between them and turned his head toward Lerd. "A furble? No one said anything about a furble."

Lerd could feel the fur on his back rising. "Didn't the Pilto tell you we need a furble too?"

"No."

Lerd stood up and began the rocking motion that Droshii affect when they are angry. "But that's impossible! I distinctly told the Pilto that I need both a grundy *and* a furble."

Mr. Herbinger picked up a pencil and began to write furiously. "I really can't apologize enough for the Pilto's oversight. However, because he is an independent agent there is very little that we can do to discipline him."

"But what can I do?"

Mr. Herbinger nervously tapped the stylus on the desk. "Well," he said, "you already have a tibbit, and we can supply the grundy. Despite the Pilto's seeming unreliability, he is really the only one who has any experience with the procurement of Droshii mates. I suggest that you go back and see him. Maybe *he* has an idea." He shook his head sadly. "We get so little call for Droshii partners. I knew this would happen one day. I told them in the front office. I said, 'One day someone is going to come in here who—'"

"Thank you for your help," Lerd said, backing out the door with Sava.

And they were gone.

The cellar stank of a ghastly mixture of off-world brews. Lerd loped quickly down the stairs and crossed to where the Pilto still sat. He lowered himself into the chair and said, "What happened?"

The Pilto looked at him innocently. "What do you mean, what happened?"

"I mean, how come Mr. Herbinger didn't know that I needed a furble?"

"He didn't . . .? That's strange. I told him quite distinctly that you needed both a grundy and a furble."

Lerd scratched at his right claw and a scaly piece of the chitin came away. He looked at it in terror. "Great Frooth!" he said.

"What's the matter?"

"Nothing." He waved his claws in the air in frustration. "Nothing at all. But you must find me a furble quickly."

"If L.U.S.T. can't help you then I don't know who can. You know how hard Droshii partners are to find."

Leaning across the table, Lerd grabbed the Pilto by his

spiny ruff and began to shake him. "You must find me a furble right now!" he cried.

The claws, still gripping the Pilto around the neck, came loose from Lerd's body. They clattered to the table. Lerd looked at them strangely and said, "It's too late . . ." His bulgy eyes flattened and he slid off the chair to the floor.

A crowd gathered around the fallen Droshii. The bartender said, "What happened?"

The Pilto prodded the unmoving body gently with a taloned foot. "He began to metamorphose. Probably knew it was coming all along. Poor gril. When he gets up in the morning he'll be a grundy."

"That's what he was looking for, wasn't it?" the bartender said.

"Yes. But it won't do him any good now. By the time he gets acclimated, his tibbit will be a f͏ ͏ ͏ ͏ "

The bartender shook his head. "He ͏ ͏ ͏ nt another tibbit then, and a gril too."

"Messy stuff, sex," the Pilto said as he peeled off a luminescent patch from his face and stuck it under his table.

The dragon stepped over Lerd's prone form and tore the patch off. He handed it back to the Pilto. "What do you think this is," he said angrily, "a nursery?"

Vonda McIntyre is a geneticist and a science fiction writer. She is also a strenuous advocate of women's lib, and I hope she will understand when I say that only a woman could have written a story as sensitive as this one. And there is more envy than male chauvinism in that statement. She describes the genesis of the story: "No connection: Collected case histories of twenty-nine messed-up kids and one who almost made it, until her parents put her in an institution. What anybody who studies genetics can't forget and usually can't do anything about. An assignment on fantasy and psychoses from Harlan Ellison. Things mesh."

Only at Night

by Vonda McIntyre

At night, when I'm here, all the babies lie quiet with their eyes closed. The ones that have eyes.

At night, covered with sheets against the whisper of air in the wards, the children begin to look almost human. I walk between the cribs of deserted newborns and the railed beds of the older ones, sometimes trying not to burst into tears. I touch them, gently, trying to soothe them. Most of them aren't capable of being soothed. They're all waiting to die. Sometimes one awakens and lies there helpless and immobile, staring up. They never cry. I hold them and wonder if they think the dull pinpoints of light on the ceiling are stars.

Tonight most of the children are awake. It might be the heat, which is too much for the air conditioning. I do what I can, touch them, change diapers (I am reprimanded if I use too many), offer water. I wish I weren't here. It's too quiet and the air is too heavy and no one's here to talk to. On other wards someone will awaken and need the reassurance of companionship to go back to sleep. Or I'll whisper a story to a child and he'll correct me if I change a line until we both begin to giggle, try to stop, and just laugh harder. But these children don't need bedtime stories. A record of gibberish would do as well. They don't need me. Maybe if they had always had love they would be able to want it and accept it now, but all they need is food and cleaning and a place out of the rain. To them I'm an automaton, wound up and set to take care of them.

I wish I weren't here at night, but the others have

been here longer and choose to come during the day. While drab sunlight seeps in they put the children on the floor to drag themselves around with stumps of limbs, like mindless invertebrates making their first foray onto the land.

I pick a child up, gently, because her skull has never grown together. There is a soft depression at the top of her head, like skin on cooled soup. I sing, more for myself than her. She is deaf.

She is watching me. My voice trails off and she blinks as if disappointed that I've stopped. Do all babies have blue eyes? I know I'm putting my own thoughts and sadnesses and fears into her gaze. She does not think; she can't. None of them can. But there's something behind her eyes that's more than complacent blankness. I put her back in her crib and move on.

I wonder if all their parents have forgotten them. They must have. They hardly ever come. . . . If I believed that I'd be a fool. Their parents remember them too well, every instant of every day, and that's why they don't come. They've spawned monsters that they're afraid to try to love. They're perfect people who hide their mistakes. If they see their deformed child before it is taken away (I've seen the parents; they can't resist one guilty peek between meshed fingers, as if they were at a freak show) they cry "Oh, God, why me?" and then they leave.

The children are restless. The ones that can move rustle their sheets. Those with limbs wave them. Twisted fingers clutch handsful of air and discard it again. I know I shouldn't be afraid, but it's very strange.

One of the larger children (I can only think of him as a large child) is strong and dully mean. Sometimes he has to be restrained with soft straps and buckles so he won't hurt himself or us. I hear him begin to beat his head against the backboard, over and over. I run down the ward. He's supposed to have an injection every night to make him sleep; they don't want me to have to handle him alone. I gave him a name because his parents didn't. He's perfectly formed and beautiful, but he has no mind and no control over bladder or bowels. I call to him, *Peter!* but he doesn't stop. He doesn't know me; he has never seen me. I take his arm and tell him gently to sit still and I try to pull him away from the backboard. His head hits again and I see his eyes when his hair flops away. They are blue . . . the same clear blue. . . .

My voice rises and I try to soften it. He'll feel my

panic like an animal and know I'm afraid. I drop the railing and take his shoulders. He's taller than I, and heavier by half. His expression when he sleeps is peaceful, but now he pulls his lips back from his teeth—the light sparks from them and blinds me. I feel tears running down my cheeks like molten ore.

He hits me. The force throws me back against another bed; I hit my head and slide to the floor. I can't get up; though I try I have as little control over my body as the children. I feel blood from my cut lip flowing out to mix with tears, and a sticky dampness spreads from the dull pain where a bed rail cut my scalp. I try to rise again and almost faint. I lie still.

I hear a clang and the sliding of sheets. I strain my eyes and see Peter crawling out of his bed. He has never been taught to walk. He seems to be coming toward and I'm afraid again, but he ignores me and flounders to the aisle between the rows of beds. He moves farther into my field of vision. I can see the other children coming and I hear the sides of cribs clanking down. I must be dreaming. The noises rise. I clench my teeth for the pain, but unlike a pinch it doesn't wake me up. I know that if I could move, or scream, or make any noise at all, this would stop. If I didn't think that I would doubt my sanity.

The children gather around Peter.

My hearing is distorted and I feel very far away. I can hear them talking but I can't make out any words. They look like a war council of ancient veterans, come to display their war wounds: missing hands and feet and ears and noses, twisted bodies, seal flippers and crab-skins, deep scars that twinge before storms. They look so absurd that I'd laugh if I could. It would be the first time I ever laughed here.

They look very angry and their voices are shrill. One of them shakes a fist of seven fingers grown together.

I wish it were day. Then I could hope for a nurse on a coffee break or a doctor on rounds or even one of the infrequent parents on pilgrimage to purge their guilt with fifteen minutes, and pity, and finally flight.

I think the children are there for a long time, but I can't really tell. I'm dizzy. My hip and shoulder hurt where they're pressed against the floor. My physical incapacity gives my imagination too much freedom: the children are plotting against me. When the doctors and the other nurses come in the morning they will find me

hanging, crucified, against the wall. I will wear a crown
of needles and catheters. I will be nude and bleeding, but
in three days I will not rise. If they can make plans of
revolt or revenge, surely they can see that I am not the
one to hate. I try to ridicule myself for taking dreams and
fancies seriously, but I'm not sure now that it's all a
dream. It seems very real. I'm frightened, and I'm trembling.

They seem to be done talking. The council roils and
breaks and moves toward me. As if I could stop them
with my eyes I watch them crawl and drool on the floor.
I brace myself . . . but they fragment their united front
and crawl away. A few of them look at me. Peter touches
my hand before he clambers up into bed. I lie here, and
slowly everything becomes quiet again.

In the morning I'm aselep and the nurses easily wake
me. I can move. I have a cut on my head and blood and a
bruise on my chin. There's a lot of blood on the floor, but
I only have a dull headache and orders to get some
stitches. I remember what happened last night. I decide
not to say anything, because they'll think I'm crazy. Peter
is lying on his back in his bed-cage, gabbling dully like a
grotesque newborn. Everything else is in order. The other
nurses ask me if I'm all right. I tell them I had a nightmare while I was unconscious and they cluck in sympathy.
One of them offers to take my shift, the inconvenient,
lonely one, at least until I'm better. I'm going to pretend
I don't notice it when she begins to regret her generosity.

They smile and the head nurse tells me to take some
time off and rest until my scalp has healed. I thank her.
After I go home I'll have to decide whether to come back
or not. . . . If I do I'll come at night. The parents only
visit in the daytime.

Ed Bryant is well represented in this volume, and for good reason. Since his summer at Clarion in 1968, he has published a couple of dozen stories and articles. He writes: "The title came first (it's one of Harlan Ellison's conversational catch-phrases), but the resultant story is nothing like I'd first envisaged. No matter. Either way, the story was intended to reflect some of the impressions California made on me during the spring of 1970. A few of the people I'd like to thank for this story are Tom Reddin, Ronald Reagan, George Putnam, Chief Davis. Oh yes—also the Vice President."

The Soft Blue
Bunny Rabbit Story

by Ed Bryant

It is April 15, 1981.

Time to render unto Caesar that which is Caesar's.

It is a happening world.

Guerrilla wars of liberation are currently flaring through Thailand, the Philippines, Anguilla, Mexico, Indonesia, Nicaragua, and so on.

It is superficially quiet in the People's Republic of Viet Nam.

But the slant-eyed devils are indeed building armed enclaves on the northern beaches of Australia, though the intelligence is not widespread.

Smaller revolutions are occurring in New York, Santa Fe, Detroit, Chicago, Denver, Los Angeles, Seattle, Albuquerque, and so on.

The top-charted tape this week in America is "Suck My Buttons."

The President's proposed Program for Civil Discipline is still tied up in the Supreme Court.

On the Santa Mira campus of the University of California the signs are out:

"HUMANE" BOMBS? BULLSHIT!

FACULTY STRIKE!

BAN PSYCHO-CHEMICAL WEAPONS

STUDENTS STRIKE!

BURN UNCLE SAM'S P-C CONTRACTS

STRIKE!

"While the iron's hot," I said.

Louise licked her finger and touched the metal. "It's hot

enough." Her soft East Texas drawl drew out the words. She spooned more batter onto Teflon squares and watched it bubble.

"I love you," I said. "Every department ought to have a lounge equipped with waffle griddle and chef. Should be one of the demands."

"The strike isn't going to work this time."

"Maybe." I stared past my window-reflection. The third floor of the Humanities Center overlooked a broad pentagonal mall. Small many-colored mannequins enjoyed the soft grass and warm afternoon as they paraded with their signs toward Admin. Between two distant slab-sided classroom buildings I saw sunlight glint back from a pigpen. I visualized the light tower and radio mast surrounded by sandbags and barbed wire. I thought I could almost see the blue uniforms and the machine guns. The clatter in the air made me look up and I saw the aircraft off above the dorms.

"Hey, Louise?"

"What." She kept her eyes on the griddle.

"A Huey. Looks like a copchopper."

Louise slapped the waffle onto a plate, then moved beside me. "How do you know?"

"A Bell UH-1. I used to fly one—ferried C-rations—back in 'Nam." I pointed. "See the black stripe? That's why I think it's a copchopper. Can't see the emblem, but it's probably Sheriff's Department."

The helicopter came in at low level. I could see wind from the blades beat ripple patterns in the grass. It made a slow circle over the mall. A few of the marchers gave it the finger. Most showed an upraised fist.

"What the hell are they doing?" I shaded my eyes with my hand. "Taking pictures?" I saw two men in the bubbled cockpit; one in uniform, one a civilian. There were tanks and nozzled gadgets strung on brackets around the outside of the fuselage.

Then the chopper leveled out and buzzed over us, out of sight. A moment later the shadow flickered across the window and nothing remained but the fading sound. Below, the Santa Mira students resumed their trek.

I felt Louise's hands on my shoulders. "Come on," she said. "Eat the damned waffle before it freezes."

So I sat down.

  I sat down.

    Sat down.

Wow. It was like a multiple-exposure film in which a

moving object leaves a trail of ghost images. I was watching me and I *was* me and finally all the trailing images of myself caught up and rejoined me. And I sat down. I inspected the waffle.

"Michael, may I ask what it is *exactly* that's wrong with the waffle?"

"Huh, Louise?" I'd never before really noticed the tiny mole under her left cheekbone. How many millimeters, I wondered, and I'm not mathematically minded. It occurred to me I could estimate by triangulation—her nose, the tip of her chin, and the mole. The square of the hypotenuse is equal to—

"Michael!"

"Louise?" What the hell was bothering her? Her eyes looked completely through me. They were bigger now, her eyes. Louise's mouth opened and worked silently as though she were crying. But no sounds, no tears. She bent over me and collapsed and one hand smashed the waffle. I held on and kept her from sliding down to the floor. Her face was still twisting and I touched her cheek. Smooth, I remembered her cheek being smooth almost like wet glass. But now I felt my fingers hang up on her pores and it was a sickening feeling like when you rub against the angle of a paper-cut and the flap of skin lifts up. My hand jerked away.

"Michaelmichaelmichael."

I didn't know my half of the litany. But—"Louise, what's wrong?"

Her eyes cut through me. My back was to the window. "Michael, the angel of death . . ." And I heard the thunder of wings.

Still clutching at each other, we struggled to the window. There, down out of the sun. There—

The *ka-chunk ka-chunk ka-chunk* of blades cleaving the air.

The flicker-flicker-flicker of vanes against the sky.

Jeweled dragonfly circling endlessly . . .

The sheep in the meadow flowed in crazy quilt colors. Running, all of them . . . Then like blows against my face the staccato explosions and I flashed on firefights in Pleiku. "Louise!" Voice was above me and to my right. "Down down get down." And dragged her down with me below the window frame as flame exploded above the mall and diamond chips twinkled over us.

The windchime tinkling subsided and we got up. The

dragonfly was twisted and burning on the grass. The
smoke had the sheen of black vinyl wrapping. People fed
the fire their signs. Some had joined hands and were
dancing a convoluted pattern of snakes mating. The
heavy odor of barbecue was in the air.

"MichaelmichaelI'msick." She pushed against me, butting her head into my shoulder, trying to hide as though
I were a grove of poplar. I slowed her words down, and
remembered that dolphins talked in speeded-up language.

"What is it?"

I burst out laughing. "Toklas waffle, love. You surprised
me."

"No." Very seriously she studied her hand, each spoke
of the mandala nimbused in waffle. "It's all here."

"Now it's not." I kissed her fingers and felt Popeye-
spinach feed into my blood. Drifts of laughter sifted
around us. I raised my arms to push back the laughter
and Louise fell to the floor quietly. Sssshh. Very, very
quiet.

On my knees: "Louise? You all right?" .   answer, but
she breathed and I felt the pulse below her ᴄ   Her eyes
screwed shut and her lips twitched.

"Help, Michael, please?" And stopped.

I stood too quickly and grazed a desk. Graded term
papers softly fell and covered her. Babe in the woods,
I'll help you, lover! I gently pulled the leaves away and
studied her face.

Until the starting gun cracked outside and I knew it
was time to start for the Health Service. I kissed her.
Then I carefully covered her up again, away from the
animals and the night wind, and left.

"Is right," said Weissburg. "And right is left. The
language of the dialectic has become so fucking confused,
man. It's the fascist press that does it." Beard and hair
hopelessly snarled, dressed in leather and green earth
colors, he was one with the soil. Rooted and organic,
totally secure in his time; Weissburg, dark tree.

I rolled over and looked for a sun that was no longer
there. The blade of grass in my mouth had the sudden
almond sting of cyanide. "Hey Jacob, how long have I
been here?"

"Years, man. Two, maybe three." He spat into the
Dixie cup and carefully stirred in the colorless crystals.

"I thought so." I let my tongue draw in another

millimeter of grass-blade and the serrated edge scarred my lip. "I've got miles to go."

"Man, you literary snobs . . ." Bemused, Weissburg drifted away. With half a single-edge razor blade he sliced gently into one of the thick blue veins of his left wrist. A delicate cut with the grain of the vein. "Shit," very softly. He pinched a beak in the rim of the Dixie cut and dripped the crystal solution into the vein. Out a long way, then snapping rubber-band back completely: "Michael, you got to get out of that department of yours. Old books oppress. They stifle, man."

Old tree, nurtured and watered now, pondered me with sad mahogany eyes.

"Hey!"

". . . amn it!"

All around us.

'Get up!"

"You!"

"Who *are* these masked men?" I was on my feet, rough hands under my armpits jerking me erect.

Weissburg's mouth smiled dreamy-soft. "I think they're the critics, man."

The masks were slick-brown and hard; the eyes wide glass, smoked expressionless like the eyes of dead men. Voices behind them came from a different land.

"Jacob Weissburg?"

"Check the photo."

"It's him."

"Do it."

Two of them grabbed Weissburg and dragged him toward the edge of the mall. His head joggled loosely. "I-don't-think-they-like-my-films."

I started after them. "Hey, what are you doing to him?" The other two masquers stopped me.

"Who is he?"

"Check his wallet."

"Meredith, Michael G."

"Not on the list."

Someone hit me from behind. I wanted to lie there and sleep, but I opened my eyes and sat up. Then I saw Weissburg against the wall and heard the volley. All bloody from groin to chest, Weissburg fell on his face in the grass and let the meadow soak him up.

I ran until I could see no more blue uniforms. Then I sat on the cold cement steps of some building and threw up before starting to mourn.

In the dark:

"Honey, why are you crying?"

"Cogito ergo sum."

"Whatever it is, you can tell me."

"Cogito ergot sum."

"Don't hold it in."

"Cogito some ergot?"

"I'm here to help you."

"I need no help," I said. "I'm hurt, but the cold and dark are my bandages."

"Are you bleeding?"

"My friend is dead," I said. "And my lover thinks she's dead."

The night-blooming street lamps furled around us.

"They hurt my eyes. Damn," said an Linda MacPherson Travis. She giggled and clapped a white hand over her mouth. "Oops, sorry. Immode language is unforgivable in—" Whatever else she said led away and was lost. She massaged her jaw gently. "I t to be very careful, you know."

"How are things in the Dean of Women's office?" I said.

"*Very* careful, you know."

"Still sending mimeoed warnings to the parents of freshman coeds dating revolutionaries?"

"Are you an immune?" She studied my face carefully.

"Dean Travis, are you aware t one of my fellow teachers is lying on her back in the English lounge? It's an infraction of the rules."

"You must be an immune."

"Oh my God," I said. "Louise." How long had I left her?

"You're a nice man. I don't mind keeping the world together for you. Really I don't."

Fucking bitch and her fucking incantatory language. Louise. How long? The Health Service. I started to get up and the Dean reached to steady me.

She screamed. "Hand!" The word echoed across the facade of the building, smashed in gray fragments on the concrete step. Dean Travis held her right wrist tightly, gingerly adjusting it as though seating a grafted limb. "Hand," she crooned.

I started to leave her.

"Help me." Her eyes were colorless and empty but I stopped. "In my bag. Get me the hand cream?"

Her handbag was a soft cornucopia, and I was distracted by the feel of things sharp and hollow. But I found the slick, cold little jar and unscrewed the lid. Her fingers dipped greedily into the white salve and she rubbed it into the pale band where evidently she had worn a wristwatch on a sunny day. "It seals the joint," she explained.

I tightly screwed the cap back on the hand cream. Dean Travis drew her legs, knees to chin, and hugged herself. I looked back once from the bottom step and she was still that way, covetous of herself in the night.

The tombstone buildings lose all identity in the dark. I searched for red crosses, but found only deserted echoing hallways. Occasionally I encountered mute men and women who hurried away. There were lights, noises, but always distant and vague. The halls narrowed, the walls were thicker.

Until someone reached through and touched my cheek with velvet.

My eyes focused under the EXIT sign: Shana, slim black fox from my romantic poetry seminar, took my hand. Silently she led me through the vertical labyrinth.

"Shana?"

Soft in softer darkness she hurried me on, hand damp in mine. In the reflection of a firestair window: eyes moist and sucking. There were no words. Then she pulled me through the door.

Music, lights, movement all tried to tear me a thousand at-once directions. Recoiling, I wanted to hide, but Shana's hand was tight in mine and I followed her.

I knew the song, though I didn't know the title or the words.

People danced, eyes looking through us toward other fantasies. We walked through them closer to the platform in the center of the gym. The group—five men with speed muses, crystal shadows behind them.

I felt the song.

The drums: a deep, deep insistent beat, a Vachel Lindsay Congo beat.

The Moog: tones, pure, that sleeted molten copper through our loins.

Guitars: shimmering razor blades sli-i-i-cing flesh.

The man on their visuals panel expanded concentric balls of hard color with the beat. No pastels; red that singed, blue that froze, searing white.

Sensual incantation . . . we danced to the rhythm, Shana and I, moving close and together. Her eyes never left mine. Sweat filmed on her skin, made it shine. Lady fox, come to me.

We danced slower, more deliberately. She started to kiss me, lips soft and swollen—

FLASHflashFLASHflash—the strobe-light and strobe-sound of machinegun fire. The music stopped raggedly, amps crackling. The visuals man bled the room with pulsing red as pigs appeared in all the doorways. In the blood-light their uniforms seemed black. They were here with their guns and lists and filtered voices.

"All right, keep calm."

"Get those lights on."

"Let's see some I.D.s."

"Line up."

"Move!"

People milled uncertainly. In slow motion I saw one of the musicians swing his guitar back over his head like an axe, then cleave the sharp leading edge down into the skull of a pig. The visuals man blacked the room. All I could see were the tracer bullets.

Shana clung to me. I dragged her through a doorway that cleared magically in the near wall. We hid behind a Coke machine while armed blue men ran past into the gym. So simple a hide-and-seek. Shana showed me a corridor to the outside. They were waiting, just inside the final door; two of them in blue, with guns. We stared at them and they back at us, and they both looked at each other.

"Get out of here," one of them said, tapping the door with the barrel of his M-20. "Now. We didn't see you."

We got out. I wondered: why do *they* have no names or faces? Is the blindness partly mine?

Indians now, we stalked from tree to tree away from the blood. Always away. Did I fear? Yes yes of course. A man faced with death or escape always picks the latter. I feared for (louise, are you still all right?) Louise in her bed of leaves. And for Weissburg (but far too late now—back to the ashes with you, jacob) also in a shallow bed. And Shana (foxy lady, i want you).

"I want you." Our bed would be soft and cool. I pulled her to me in the scent of spruce and she lifted her arms as I pulled her dress up and off.

The spiny clicking, behind us . . . Turning very slowly I discovered our bedroom was in a children's playground with swings and seesaws and climbing bars skeletal in the moonlight.

Dark planes, mysterious hollows, she stepped back and watched me undress.

In the foreground was a toy for climbing; a steel disk with painted eyes, supported by eight double-jointed legs. I looked beyond it for the noise, the clicking and rasp. Something moved in the periphery of my vision, close.

Her mouth was no longer gentle and I pulled her head away from my neck.

Playground equipment, sinister but harmless. My eyes kept sweeping, back and forth, and still the movement tantalized there in the corner of sight.

Shana shook straight hair back from her face; her lips moved silently, shaping softness. On my knees, astraddle her thighs, I felt small breasts crush against my chest.

Screaming screaming it leaped out of the moonlight where I couldn't quite see it and ripped at me with spiny, articulated legs. Horror of endless children's nightmares —I tore at it.

I thrust her down against ragged grass and broken pine twigs. She writhed to free her legs and then wrapped them ar ̶ ̶d me.

Horror   chittered from the choking dust of old attics and clinging webs in dark basements. It wrapped around me, throbbing; faceted onyx eyes stared into my own.

She helped me; there was no need. It was slick and warm. Shana's mouth fastened on mine.

I screamed, and couldn't hear the sound. I tore at the thing with my fingernails and wrenched my head back, away from the slashing mandibles. It hissed, lunging for my throat.

Shana moaned, arched her back. I knew I would come the same time as she.

It had a throat; I found it and squeezed. It had a body and I bent it back against itself until it broke like dry branches snapping. I hurt it and crushed it and it screamed.

We moved faster; we reached and clung; she bit my throat and raked her nails down my back; harder I slammed her against grass and twigs; she screamed a long shuddering cry in the moonlight.

Now:

Sometime before dawn, the wind blows off the ocean and cleans impurities from the land. Naked, I walk along the beach letting my lungs cleanse themselves. The wind is cold and cuts away the last spiderwebs in my head.

I stop at the crest of the highest dune and feel sand sift away beneath my toes. How easily foundations slip. As long as I face this direction I see only the ocean. I feel the sun rising behind me.

Vaguely I know where the university is, and the town of Santa Mira. I ignore the monstrous shadows. For now I face the sea.

Soon I will turn around.

Dreamers on the Barricades

by Harlan Ellison

Walking the Stanford campus after it had been trashed during a "student riot," I was dismayed to see that the Earth Sciences Building had been severely ravaged: windows broken to the last pane, walls fire-mottled, doors boarded up. I was at Stanford to lecture and knew that at least a portion of my talk on "Speculative Fiction as Street Literature for a Time of Dissent and Revolution" would be concerned with student demonstrations. And while, on the whole, I approve of such outpourings of feeling, I was horrified that libraries and ostensibly "uncommitted" buildings could get caught in the scattergun blasts of anger and frustration.

I said as much to Professor Bruce Franklin, a scholar in both sf and revolutionary literature. He hardly paused as we walked toward the faculty dining room, but his off-hand remark brought me to a halt: "Almost everything being done in that building in the name of 'earth science' is paid for by the oil companies; it's research to help them better rape the planet. The kids knew it and they said so."

That their method of verbalizing their fury at the corruption and exploitation of their university was a violent and destructive one is a matter that can be debated and/or deplored. But it certainly made the point. A point even I, considering myself a militant, had never realized. The kids *knew*. They were at the core of our crippled society's heart, and they *knew* that good can be used to promote evil. They knew that the research chemists and geologists in that building were taking the copout route that has become *de rigueur* with scientists since the Manhattan Project: I'm only doing research; application isn't my fault or concern.

They had heard the same words from the mouth of Adolf Eichmann: I'm only doing my job. And they knew it was a hype. So if the scientists in that building wouldn't shoulder their responsibility to the world and its people, being mired down ever more each year in an ecological morass, then they would show them the way. So they burned the building. It was a sad-making, possibly deplorable, but certainly effective point-maker.

Making points as hard to handle as the one impressed on me at Stanford is an unwritten rule for the students of the Clarion Workshop in Fantasy & SF. They want writers of speculative fiction, but they are children of their times as well. Because of this wholly compatible dual allegiance, they bring to their craft a verve, a fire, a ferocity that is unhappily absent in all but a handful of the writers in the genre who have gone before them.

They need not even explicate—as I do here—that one of their important chores as creators of verbal magics is to very literally (and literarily) alter the course of human destiny, to change the world, to shake up their society, to start people thinking and, if possible, drive them to the barricades in defense of true mortal freedom and a decent world in which to live.

They work in a fine tradition. Zola, Hugo, Dickens, Frank Norris, Harriet Beecher Stowe, Wells, London, Mark Twain, and, of course, Bernard Shaw all used their fiction to make unpleasant but necessary comment on the condition of life. It is nothing new to speculative fiction. Our people have been doing it since the earliest days of the form. For instance: ecology? Hell, the brouhaha today in which every strap-hanger and shopgirl speaks knowledgeably about biodegradible this and pollutive that was pre-dated by (to grab a quick reference that comes readily to mind) John Christopher in 1956 with his classic sf novel, *No Blade of Grass.*

But the important sf writers of today, and the fast guns of Clarion, learning their craft systematically and preparing themselves to facedown with those of us currently working in the form, have gone far beyond such cautionary tales. The comparison between sf writers of yesterday and those of today—as exemplified by the young writers in this book—is the comparison between civil-rights dissenters of ten years ago who chose to credit "the enemy" with nobility and reason, and settled for lunchroom sit-ins and Martin Luther King's passive resistance . . . and the revolutionaries of today who *know* the Silent Majority of Mr. Agnew would rather abrogate their responsibilities by ignoring the evils that abound and clinging to some mythical status quo that hasn't existed in this country for one hundred and twenty years . . . revolutionaries who burn the Bank of America in Isla Vista because they know the only way to move the society *at all* is to offer a hideous alternative to "the feast of reason and the flow of soul" (in Pope's felicitous phrase).

The revolutionary writers of sf hurl fire and thunder and lightning in their work. No longer satisfied to merely point an accusing finger or cluck a reprimand, they serve with their tales of today and tomorrow to galvanize an apathetic world into action.

Oddly enough, they are a peace generation. They have been brought up on the unceasing lies and charades of mass-media dissemination of information (and so, wryly, they are a TV generation as well). They know that we, older and "wiser," have come through corruption and compromise to an intellectual stance in which we take the napalm deaths of tens of thousands as just another seven-o'clock report. They are not willing to abide in such a world.

So while their less-talented brothers and sisters merely demonstrate and parade, they add to such mundane pursuits with their stories. They operate not only as human beings, but as creators. They fulfill the noblest objectives of *art* while paying heed to the uses such works serve as *propaganda*. They know that the first, the primary, obligation is to the Muse of Creativity but they also fully comprehend the life demands of the God of Change. (I have had this discussion many times with other sf writers who feel an artist's sole job is to create, that propagandizing only cheapens the intent and final judgment of posterity on the work. To all these discussions I bring the [to me] irrefutable example of Picasso's "Guernica," a painting of such brilliance that it stops the breath in one's throat. Picasso wrought it from his need to say something potent about the horrors of war, and though one can study it today and know *nothing* of its origins, the *art* remains. And thus I arrive at the foundation of my theory about art as a vehicle for dissent: the fury and purity of the creator's need to *say something* motivates the work, but he forms it from logic and craft and honesty and when

the propaganda value has faded into last week's impera-
tive, the *art* remains behind and stands on its own merits.)

I use the word "art" repeatedly in speaking about speculative fiction, particularly as rendered by these Clarion
writers. It is not a handy-word. I use it purposely. For it
seems obvious to me—and will seem so, hopefully, to you
upon having read the stories contained herein—that these
young writers have grasped the truth that sf is one of the
few viable forms of speaking out available to us today.
They are not hamstrung as their older brothers and sisters
in the sf idiom have been, by the belief that sf was merely
escapist fiction. They have seen how many college students
read and honor speculative fiction. They have seen the
growing importance as a legitimate species of literature
that sf has achieved. They have seen it taught in universities
and they have read the scholarly works on the subject.

And now they come to it without the years of blindness
and compromise through which we older writers have
trudged. They come to it with a purpose. To inform, to
enlighten, to radicalize, and to compel to action.

I submit these Clarion writers are in the noblest traditions of those who have dealt with High Art.

They are young, and they are naive in many ways, but
like their generation they are our best hope. They dream
elegant dreams of tomorrows in which the words ICBM,
Middle East crisis, Mace, hardhat, hippie, confrontation
and reactionary are never spoken. They dream their
dreams of joy and wonder—and blood and fire as well—
to the end that, like all great artists, they may point us
toward a horizon where no smoke spirals to a deadly gray
sky.

They are dreamers first, but they are fighters as well.

How much more can we ask of the young?

Bob Thurston is a quiet man in his thirties who gave up professoring to become a full-time writer. His contributions to this volume demonstrate what a good decision that was. I suspect that this story—winner of the NAL first prize—grew from Bob's own love-hate relationship with one of its central characters, the battered 1967 Mustang he once owned.

He writes: "In my lifetime the mythology surrounding cars has undergone some change. Years ago getting your own automobile meant that you had taken a significant step upward toward confidence, power, and sexual mastery. In the present time of pollution-consciousness and traffic jams lined up to infinity in parallel lanes, the adventure of driving is gone for many motorists. While advertising still strives to convince us that a new car is a sure route to confidence, power, and especially sexual mastery, such fantasies are hard to hold onto when breathing the wastes of the steed in front of you and listening to the knight behind you leaning on his horn."

Wheels

by Robert Thurston

Got to have wheels. No other out, no other escape from this. Lincoln Rockwell X says he can get me a car. Only catch, I got to go to the ghetto for it.

I might get wheels all right, but I might drive out dead. Still—if I don't do anything about it now, I'll be too old when I can.

I'll never get a safedry license anyhow. You got to be the son of a safedry. They'll shove you that crap about safedry's high life expectancy, being hereditary, just to hide what's true, that it's all kissass games. My father's screwed me royal. He's a known traffic vile. I been turned down now seventeen times for a learner's permit. Bureau clerks laugh among themselves when I come in.

I want to have wheels, I go to the ghetto. Today.

Bus clerk, bastard, turned me down. No seats available. Had to walk crosstown. Three or four carloads of punk safedrys out cruising. They shout insults at me. Can't offer to fight them 'cause I'm alone. Crummy bastards, they drive through the streets, their windows locked tight when they're not throwing out challenges, when they're not throwing out rocks, their bodies moving to music we can't hear through the soundproofing.

At least it's not night. At night, in areas police cars avoid, they search us out and scare us by backing us against walls with their cars. They come up on the pavement after us. We steal their license plates when we can. We bend them out of shape and bury them in the ground.

Street debris clings to my trousers. Dust flies into my

47

eyes. I need something different. My whole life needs a kick in the balls. Work is sleepwalking from desk to desk. Home is sneaking looks at my father sneaking drinks. Play is dodging the traps, play is bumping bodies to drumbeats you can't hear. Sex is just bumping bodies. The cops may crack me for illegal driving. But they got to catch me first.

Easy time slipping past the pig line, crawling across the rubble of the abandoned buildings. I walk through the sniper zone unscathed (a distant shot keeps me alert) and meet Lincoln Rockwell X at the designated streetcorner. Blackfolk stare at me but leave me alone. Only an idiot sneaks into their territory, Lincoln Rockwell X says, and they don't think it's Christian to maim idiots. Don't let them know you're not an idiot, he says. I walk along with my tongue sticking out the corner of my mouth.

Lincoln Rockwell X leads me to wheels. It's in the basement of an abandoned Afro-Methodist church. We have to maneuver around upended and broken pews. To get to the car we have to go down steps behind what's left of an altar. We pass office doors with broken windows. You can see only junk inside.

He takes me to a recreation room. No electricity, he says, I'll light candles and you get the Big Show, dig? He makes an elaborate thing out of placing the candles on the stage. Lights each one with a swishy hand move. He sings a trumpet call through his nose as he opens a curtain that's got burn holes all over it.

And there you go, he says. Wheels.

Which is so, though it's not exactly like I imagined it. All the cars you see on the street are shined-up no matter how old they are. Safedrys think a glossy car's better than a big prick. And they don't allow any bumps anywhere on the body of the car. If anything happens, they quick get to a garage before anybody finds out and they got points against them. They'll pay anything to keep their record clean, to keep their license.

But this car! This car's got pain in every curve. It'd choked to death and gone to hell. It looked menacing. Like if you touched it, you'd get cancer.

Five hundred dollars, says Lincoln Rockwell X.

Five hundred dollars? I say. For *that*?

You got a better deal, you go make it. No small talk on my time, man.

I know better than to argue. I'm deep in his territory,

more than five hundred bucks in my pocket. Lincoln Rockwell X's got blades for teeth. Sight unseen I'd already bought this baby.

Still—I make like a reluctant buyer. I walk around the car. I kick a tire; it wraps rubber around my foot. I grab a door handle which almost comes off in my hand.

What do I know about cars? Nothing. But I pretend.

What year? I ask.

'67, he says.

'67 what?

'67 Mustang. Saved from a graveyard and reconditioned in '75. My granddaddy did the job himself.

'75. That was the year they stopped carmaking altogether.

No, man. Ford kept going till '79. Went down fighting.

I brush away a layer of dirt. The car is dark green underneath. Dark green where it's not rust. I run a finger along the fold-line of a dent. Dark-green flecks come off onto my fingertip.

Jeez, how'm I gonna drive this heap around? Look at all the dents. Cops'll crack me in a minute.

Your PR with the fuzz is your business, baby. You wanted wheels, these're the only bootleg wheels left in town. You got five hundred dollars, you got wheels. You can leave the small talk in your wallet.

Okay, okay, but how'm I gonna get this junkpile on the street? Drive it through the ceiling?

You got five hundred, I'll open sesame for free.

I open the door real easy and get in. Dashboard's in scarred leather. Seats are ripped bad, too. A part of the steering wheel's missing, making it look like a broken-off piece of pretzel. I try out the accelerator. Creaks on the down motion, cries on the up. I move the automatic floor shift, the only undamaged part of the car.

I tell Lincoln Rockwell X okay I'll take it, and hand him the five bills. He takes over the driver's seat. He produces the key with another swishy flourish and puts it in the ignition. The car moans, gurgles, trembles, threatens suicide, but doesn't start.

Don't worry boy, Lincoln Rockwell X says. Cars're like this when they're not used every day.

He invokes a tribal curse and re-presses the accelerator. The car curses back but gives in.

He gets the car out of the building through use of a freight elevator at the back of the stage.

Up a ramp and out in the light, I get my first good look

at my wheels. I see all the bumps and dents I missed in candlelight. The thing looks like a crumpled piece of paper. Front and back windows both have cracks in them. Headlights point in opposite directions. Fenders are separating at the seams. Bumper's rippled like sea waves. The mustang on the insignia's laid down and died. Another hole in the roof and it'll be a convertible.

How you ever had this heap on the road I'll never know, I tell Lincoln Rockwell X.

Around here cops see a car in this condition riding the asphalt, they lay off cause they know the driver's got blades for fingers.

But how'm I gonna get it across the police lines?

You own the car now, man, you make it run wherever you want to make it go. There's gas cans in the trunk. Call me when you need more.

But where'll I take it?

Take it anywhere but keep it moving. Only white allowed around here gotta be blurred.

You have a responsibility to me.

Shove that, man. I put you in the motherfucker seat and that's all is necessary.

He walks away, waving the five bills like a flag. I locate the horn, push it in to get his attention. It wheezes shyly but makes no other sound. I'll get out, run after him, snatch the five bills, run like hell. The door handle comes off in my hand.

I've had the course. What can I do? Stay in the ghetto, dodge between blades? Race cops around the city? Drive only on moonless nights?

My Mustang, motor running, has a coughing fit. I quick depress the accelerator, run it hard to keep the engine from dying out. The accelerator pedal vibrates. The whole car begins to shake.

I better get this car moving before it really gets angry. I shift to D, press the accelerator pedal. A delay before the car responds, then a growling jump forward. Spinning tires set gravel flying, striking the underside of the car with hollow clanging noises.

Ghetto streets make good practice runways. I see only two other cars, each dilapidated, though in better condition than the Mustang. The streets are filled with obstacles— potholes, chunks of broken pavement, jagged trash. People jump into doorways when I drive along the sidewalk.

The Mustang is reluctant. When I try to gun the motor, it groans and waits a second before granting the speed increase. None of the dashboard gauges work right. The gas gauge doesn't work at all. Maybe I should just joyride, let the gas run out and abandon the car. Kiss the five bills goodbye.

Getting through the police line is easy. Both cops're busy beating up a spade rummy. They got him backed up against a piece of building and they're trading off who slams the club into his gut. The black man shouts out old militant slogans. A carfull of white kids parked on the safe side of the line call out ratings for each blow. I speed by them and they hardly glance at me.

The Mustang, which rattles a lot at slow speeds, quiets down with acceleration. I never drove a car before, but my father described driving to me and one time I rode with a social worker and watched everything he did. I make a few mistakes now but I learn fast.

I can't go home now with no place to hide wheels. If I keep driving around the city, I'll have fuzz scrambling around the windshield in an hour or two. Or the night-roamers'll run me off the road once they see the car's illegal.

It took almost three workdays to get the five bills, so I might as well get some value for my money. I'll take a chance, drive around till   thing happens. What can happen? I can get the shit beat out of me, that's what. I can get five to twenty for driving without a license, another rap for the illegal vehicle itself. I can get sliced up. I can die.

Still—what's a few risks if you got wheels?

Suddenly I'm in the country. Open fields, overhanging trees, telephone poles, soft shoulders, road signs—the works. I look in the rearview mirror to make sure the city's still behind me, that it hasn't disappeared. The change is too fast, too abrupt. I'd expected a police line, or some barrier, a sign saying This Is the Countryside.

I begin to notice signs at the side of the road; around a circle each says To the Expressway. Inside the circle is an arrow pointing the way. We got expressways in the city, great cracked-up roads with their entrances blocked off with walls. Kids play on them 'cause they're safe. I decide to check this expressway out.

I give the Mustang its head. I slam down on the accelerator. Gradually the car picks up speed, I don't know how much because the speedometer needle jams at 50 mph. At a certain speed the car begins to vibrate menacingly. I slow it down to the fastest safe speed.

The car has a tendency to veer to the right. I have to clutch the steering wheel to keep the car on the road. I'm learning that the Mustang does what it wants to do. I have no control over it, I just make suggestions and hang on.

I pass another car, wheels screaming. Scared, I look in the rearview mirror. The other car kicks into action and ins to follow me. I push the pedal to the floorboards. rating like hell the Mustang goes faster, reaches its top eed. It is not enough. My wreck of a Mustang is no hatch for the sleek tuned-up model chasing us. I try evasive tactics, hogging the middle of the road so that our pursuer can't pass. Around a curve he glides to the outside, comes alongside, and convinces us to pull over.

You can read fuzz all over his face. He's skinny but he walks like a fat man. His little eyes look out between the only bulges in his face. Cram-course muscles hang from his thin shoulders like meat on hooks.

He pulls open my door. It makes a loud snap like it's going to break off. He grabs my collar with huge hands id drags me out of the car. My feet get tangled and I start to fall. He tosses me the rest of the way. I hit my head against a rear fender. The pain makes everything blur.

You pukes're getting braver all the time, he says.

I don't know what you're talking about.

I'm talking, you asshole, about how far you're willing to venture from the Cloverleaf. Which group of bums you belong to—the Roadrunners, the Mechs, the Hundred-plussers?

I tell him I don't understand. I stand up. He gives a kind of nasal grunt and slaps me across the face backhand. He grabs my shoulders, twists me around, pushes me against the trunk. I double over, a sharp fender edge caving in my stomach. He frisks me, takes away my wallet. I start to stand up. He pushes me down. Pinpoints of colored light flash like TV interference and I black out.

As I wake up, I hear the cop saying:

Get your ass here pronto. I can't sit on the lid all day just for this jerk. Okay, okay. Ten-four.

I'm laid out on the ground, on my back. He must've put me there, arranged me carefully like an undertaker with a corpse he really likes.

You okay, old buddy? he says.

I test all my breakable parts.

Yeah. Okay.

Stupid, you shouldn't take such chances.

Chances?

When you got a gang, stay with them. You guys that think you can go it on your own—why, that car of yours couldn't outrun a fat nurse pushing a baby buggy.

I don't get it.

What are you trying, getting off on a schmuck defense? Stupid's not an excuse. We're not going to baby you jerks any more. Any day now, we're going to tear up the roads and pour your skulls into the new cement.

His voice is strange. Like, he's telling me how his side is going to brutalize me and he sounds like he's giving me friendly advice.

I sit up. He leans against a car door, puffing a joint.

Funny, you don't look like a jerk. You're not Fu enough.

He hands me the joint. I try not to look surprised. I accept it and take a big drag. It makes the pains better.

You look like a guy who used to be my partner on a city beat. We'd go off to a coop and rap about things. He didn't know shit about being a good cop but he read a lot and could tell me in a few words what he read.

I pass back the joint. His fingers are so big he can hardly take it out of my hand.

He'd been one of you jerks, maybe that's why you remind me of him. He could explain the radical line so it almost made sense. Shit, I think he figured on revolutionizing the force.

He takes another drag, holds it for a long time.

Nice kid. Got sliced from hairline to heel by some punk out looking for wheels to cop. Ain't run with a partner since.

I hold onto a fender of the Mustang and pull myself up. The fender almost breaks off under the strain of my weight. My gut feels like it's ripped to pieces.

You'll be okay, kid. Just be glad I didn't give you my patented Sergeant Allen special. They can't get up from that—they beg for amputations.

You Sergeant Allen?

Yeah. You heard of me?

No.

He seems disappointed.

You ain't been on the road long then, he says.

I look around. We're in the middle of the curve. You can't see far either way.

You got any information, I can see you get off easy.

He seems embarrassed to be saying it.

No. I don't know shit. Really.

He gives me a strange smile, like he likes the answer.

Ah, you jerks, he says, and I think he means something good.

I wonder if he's jazzing me. He talks like no pig I ever heard. I mean, he makes me want to talk to him. I decide to.

You like being a cop?

He laughs. An explosion.

You really are a dumbass from the word go. Shit, I bet if we still had to read off the rights for you jerks, I'd have to spell out every word for you.

I don't understand, but I'm learning it's better to keep my mouth shut. He takes a last drag on the joint, then crushes it between his big fingers and throws it away.

I hear the sound of an approaching car. I wonder how long I've been hearing it. Allen's only senses. He reaches in his glove compartment and pulls out a gun. I haven't seen a gun up close since I was thirteen. This one has a short barrel and a thick grip. Allen holds it like he wants to use it.

Squad car's coming from town, he says, ain't nobody else out here on patrol. So that must be buddies of yours. You got something arranged, jerk?

I can't tell him the only arrangement I ever made is buying this screwed up car.

The sound stops just around the curve. Car doors open and slam. Feet glide across gravel. Moving shadows through a clump of trees.

I hear you, you stupid bastards, Allen shouts. I don't know what you're up to but I got four clubs joining me any minute.

As if to prove his statement, a siren begins to sound in the distance. I see something on the other side of the Mustang, a dark blur in the bushes. I look to see if Allen noticed. No, he's watching the other side of the road. His body's crouched. The siren gets louder.

Rescuing this dummy's not worth your time, Allen shouts.

Something flies out of the bushes at me. It comes at me chest-level and I catch it. I look down. It's a monkey wrench. A flying monkey wrench. I look at Allen; he hasn't seen. The siren sounds very close. The dark blur jumps silently out of the bushes and crouches beyond the Mustang. I walk three steps to Allen. He hears only the last step and turns. I swing the wrench backhanded, hit the side of his head, scrape the wrench across his forehead, hit him a second time cheekbone level.

Get moving, calls a voice behind me. The siren sounds like it's next door. I run to the Mustang, climb in, too panicked to look at the dark blur, who now occupies the other front seat. I turn the ignition key. The motor wheezes.

Get moving, you dumb shit, says the dark blur, hitting the dashboard with both fists. I can tell by the voice it's a girl. The Mustang must be scared of her, 'cause it starts up right away.

I push the Mustang to its limit. Every time I think it's having its death rattle, instead it finds a new resource of power and keeps going. The other car, the one from around the curve, joins us and we ride side by side down the highway. Four guys are in the other car. They wave and make odd signs at me.

This car's out of sight *bad*, my companion says. What you got under the hood, a rusty sewing-machine motor?

I look over at her, try to examine what can be seen of her. Which isn't much 'cause she's so small. She's black. Very dark, so I suspect she wears a darkening makeup, the kind they advertise as AfroBlack.

Keep your motherfucking eyes on the road, she says. Up ahead it's all broken up and you got to ride the shoulder. It's only a mile to the Cloverleaf.

I continue to sneak looks at her.

Where'd you guys come from? I say. How'd you know Allen had me?

She has white-girl-texture hair and she ties it back as if ashamed of it.

We keep tabs, she says. We got a good lookout post up in the hills with a highpower telescope. They saw Allen beating up on you.

She has a white girl's small-nostril nose, but the lips are right.

What's your name? I say.

She has childlike shoulders and arms, a series of round pipes with ball-bearing joints.

Cora. Cora Natalie Townsend. What's yours?

She has practically no tits at all, just a hint of nipple beneath a tight sweater.

Lee Kestner.

She has thin but well-proportioned legs.
I want to see her eyes but she won't look at me.

We come to the Cloverleaf. The other car speeds ahead
and leads me through its maze. We cross a bridge. Down
below are eight lanes of highway, four on each side of a
center mall. I see at least three abandoned cars at the sides
of the road but not a moving vehicle from one horizon to
the other.

This the Expressway? I say.

Shit, you really *don't* know. Where you come from, a
cave?

No, I just never been out of the city before.

You mean to tell me you never rode the Expressway?

s.

ell you're about to now. I should've known when I saw
his rotten car that you were a dumb shit newcomer. Because it's so slow. Newcomers' cars're lucky if they do 75
on a straightaway.

I just bought this car.

You *paid* for this wreck? Boy, you may be the Newcomer of All Time.

The other car stops by a Merge sign. Its driver rolls
down a window. Cora tells me to stop.

The Savarin? the other driver shouts.

The Savarin, she shouts back.

As the other car pulls away, picking up speed fast, she
says:

Chuck's impatient. Doesn't want to drag along at your
speed. He doesn't believe in wet-nursing other vehicles,
      ves them on their own. C'mon, let's see how fast this
      cart can go.

She looks at me and I see her eyes. They are dark,
expre   . They say, you fool with me and I'll slice off
whateve.   rt of you I want.

We go to   Savarin, Cora cursing the Mustang all the
way. The Sava   is on top of a hill at the end of a long
curved access road. Parked around it are more cars than
I've ever seen at one time. Some of them are being worked
on. Others have people sitting in them, on them, leaning
against them, eating off them.

With so many cars *here,* how come you don't see any
on the road?

Cora gives me a dumb-shit look.

Two reasons. One, to conserve gas and materials, which

are becoming harder to get and more expensive all the
time. The legal service stations that deal on the side charge
an arm and leg just to negotiate. Two, it's safer to travel at
night. In the daytime we're more vulnerable to sneak at-
tacks from the fuzz. Once we're on the highway they see us
as legal game and they get all kinds of plaudits when they
round up a few of us.

Why don't they just come here and get a bunch of you
all at once?

Too many of us, not enough of them. It's volunteer duty
out here: the smart pigs stay in the city and they can only
get a few freaks like Allen to take country duty. Anyway,
they like to keep us as far outside the city as they can, no
room for us in the jails or the camps any more. So they
don't bug us much. They hide at the access roads and
exits, and look for strays. They only attack when the odds
are in their favor. Except Allen. He wants our blood and
he wants it flowing. C'mon, I'm going to introduce you to
the one man you need desperately right now.

She takes me to a tall, heavy-set man in grease-stained
coveralls.

This is The Mech, she says, some reverence in her voice.
If anyone can resuscitate that corpse you drive, he can.

The Mech says he'll get to it later. Cora and I go into
the Savarin.

She introduces me to a lot of people and then sits me
down at the remains of a counter to eat. The room is
crowded. Some people sleep in cots lined along the wall.
Children run in and out. One man works on a long poem
which he is inscribing in Magic Marker around an enormous coffee percolator.

Cora seems to look for an excuse to escape from me. I
set traps to keep her with me.

I want to touch her—but so she'll know I touched her
because I wanted to. Instead I brush against her arm
reaching for a sugar shaker, graze knees while swaying the
counterstool.

This Allen, he's mean, huh?

Mean? Yeah. Yeah, I guess. He's tough. He can scramble
your brains with one punch if he wants to. But you got to
respect him.

I don't understand.

You wouldn't. See, he's a loner and they're hard to
come by out here. Most of the time, they cram four-five
pigs into one car, but he comes after us all by himself. He
digs it, taking us on by himself. He's a spooky dude.

You ever had a run-in with him?

Once. Almost took a bunch of us in. He was pretty nice to me, told me some legal tricks I might use.

Outside, a score of engines start up. Nervous laughter and fidgeting indicate the eagerness of the crowd to hit the road.

We go out to check if The Mech's revived the Mustang. He's taken it inside the garage part of the Savarin building. Crouched over the engine, he's taking pieces out and throwing them over his shoulder. Parts lie scattered all around him on the concrete floor. When he sees us, he says:

Not ready yet. Got a lot to do before I can make this baby even run a straight line wtihout wobbling.

Is it salvageable? I say.

It's salvageable all right. But never expect it to chase rabbits. With new parts and a tune-up and a speed booster, it might hit 85 or 90 but you can give up any hopes of it being a hundredplusser.

So long as it runs on more than wishful thinking I'll be satisfied.

As night falls, cars leave the parking area, usually in groups of four or five.

Any more crowds their piece of road, Cora says.

Where do they go?

Anywhere.

I mean why do they go out on the road at all?

The dumb-shit look again.

They got to, she says.

The Savarin empties, becomes barnlike in its emptiness. Cora and I sit in a booth. She wants to get out on the road, you can see that in her fumbling hands, her overeager smiles, the vacant look in her eyes. Many people invite her to ride, but she says no.

I hate being just a rider, she says. I had my own car but I smashed it against an abutment. I'll get wheels again, soon's I find a deal.

Many accidents along this road?

Not many. Sometimes a spinoff or a car that dies completely. Not many fatalities. We take care of our own when anything happens. If only the cops'd leave us alone completely.

We don't talk much now. I watch the front of her sweater, trying to locate the shape of breasts behind the nipples. She is so tiny. Standing up, she comes to chest-level on me. She must weigh under a hundred pounds.

The Mech comes into the Savarin. He announces that all transplants have been made and the car still lives. He won't take money, but he accepts half the cans of gas in the trunk. At the garage I notice that he'd already taken them.

Shall we try her out? I say, patting the Mustang on the hood.

We better wait. Till somebody can drive out with us.

I don't want to run in packs. Look, you heard what The Mech said, it can't even go as fast as other cars. Who'd drive out with us? Who wants to wet-nurse slower vehicles?

I don't know. It's risky.

Good, let's go.

She's hot for it, I can see that. She looks at the Mustang like it's a souped-up racer. I take her hand, a legal touch, and lead her to the car.

I slam down the accelerator. A roar shakes the whole car. I take it down the exit ramp and onto the main highway, giving it a little gas at a time, letting it speed up by degrees.

The Mech's done a good job. I can feel a thousand little differences. The steering's steadier, the engine smoother, the car's responses more immediate. It holds the road with sureness. Cora flicks a switch and the goddamned radio works. She finds a program of chant-rock. The heavy beat underscores the evenness of the Mustang's ride.

Finally I hit top speed, glancing sideways to see if Cora's impressed. She isn't. As the Mech says, the car's not going to set any speed records, but it does glide along. We enter a stretch of road with woods on each side; shadow trees fly by. We pass several abandoned cars, some with their hoods up, many with windows broken, most apparently stripped of valuable items.

The scenery flashing by, the car rumbling pleasantly around me, I think of making it with Cora. I glance over at her, trying to devise a way in which fantasy might meet reality. She smiles at me, a hopeful sign. I reach out my hand. She squeezes it, but does not hold it, a gesture more like affirmation of brotherhood than love.

Still—she's here in the car with me, and we're cutting a wide slice through the night. I'm better off than when I didn't have wheels.

As we leave the wooded area, a metallic glint of light flashes through the last trees. Cora doesn't see it and I don't say anything. I alternate looking at the sideview and rearview mirrors. Another ray of light, but this time not in the forest. Out on the road this time. The third gleam and whatever it is, is closer to us. The Mustang is already going as fast as it will go. I try to nudge the pedal further into the floorboards. A sign informs me it is twenty-three miles to the next rest area. Cora senses my tension. She twists around, looks out the back window.

What's back there? she says.

I'm not sure.

Dumb-shit look.

It's another car, I guess.

You guess?! It's a pig car. It's Allen, it's got to be. He's the only one with nerve enough to buzz this stretch.

What'll we do?

I don't know, I can't think—keep going straight ahead till something happens. He's got the speed, but it'll still take him a few miles to catch up.

Maybe we should ditch the car, make a run for it.

Shit, I got to be in a spot like this with an idiot who don't know his ass from a crack in the road. It's open country here. We'd never get far. We'll have to chance what comes. Keep driving.

It catches up with us quicker than she'd guessed. It slows down behind us, staying on our tail but far enough back to remain a black ghost. A black ghost, its headlights off, stalking us.

It's Allen all right, Cora says. He likes fun and games. We got to make the first move. Hit the brake.

What?

Hit the brake, shithead!

We burn rubber in a long skid but hold our lane. The other car eases past us. He's in front of us before he realizes what happened. His brake lights flash on, but we're controlling speed now. He tries to slow but we stay right on his tail. With four lanes leeway he can't set up a block or run us off the road. He guns his motor and pulls away from us.

Okay, Cora says, we've got him taking a chance.

Let's turn around, head back.

Can't, too risky. He'd catch up. No, forward's best. We have to wait him out.

As she gives me the instructions, I feel really stupid. She speaks to me as if I'm a kid.

She's tense. She hugs her legs to her chest.

Maybe we should slow down and get off the road, I say. Maybe he won't try to find us.

No, if he did get to us, we wouldn't have a chance. Shut off the headlights so at least he won't see us coming for miles.

I can barely see the road in the dim moonlight. The Mustang hums steadily, going along at about 40 mph. A couple of times it slides off the road onto the shoulder but most of the time finds its own way as if it had built in radar.

Maybe you should pull over, Cora says, and let me drive.

I don't say anything, just keep going. She mutters something that I'm glad I can't understand. I roll down a window, listen to night noises. A shadowy blur turns out to be nothing more than a shadowy blur. I slow down further. To my left we seem to pass the sound of a quiet engine idling. The sound skips and I hear tires against gravel.

Open her up, Cora screams.

I increase speed. I have to turn the headlights on again again so I can see where I'm going. He flashes his on, too. So he can take aim, as it turns out. The first shot, although it doesn't hit anything, is close enough to frighten me. I get a quick mental picture of Allen, leaning out the window and taking aim, a fat hand around the tiny gun, the other hand on the steering wheel. An anatomical absurdity, but if it's Allen, it's probably what he's doing.

I swerve but regain control. Next shot goes through the back window, leaving a circular area in white-lined little fragments. A third ricochets off the side of the car.

Switch lanes, Cora shouts, and keep switching.

I start zigzagging. He guns his motor and comes up even with me on the outside.

Get out of his way, damn it, Cora shouts.

He sideswipes me. A terrifying crunch of metal. I almost go into a spin, but the Mustang responds and I ease back into a lane. Through my sideview I see that he's had the worst of the swipe. Body damage my Mustang can take in stride. He's skidded sideways and has to straighten out. I feel a weird sense of satisfaction, but can only hold it for a second because he's catching up again.

I pass a sign. Exit, Food, Gas, Lodging, one mile. I keep dodging from lane to lane.

Exit, ½ mile.

We'll get off there, I say.

Cora looks terrified.

No, you dumb shit.

Why the hell not?

He'll cream you there. That's his territory, man.

What the fuck are we supposed to do? He'll cream us here.

I'll think of something.

I already have.

I let him almost catch up. At the last minute I swerve onto the exit ramp. He overshoots it. His tires scream as he turns around. Cora screams at me, but I can't make out what she's saying. I go around the long curve, over the bridge. Behind me I can see Allen's car at the far curve of the exit ramp. I turn right onto the access road and floor the pedal. The Mustang makes the long curve. On two wheels, it feels like. I mutter long, involved promises to it. Under the bridge I execute a skidding U-turn and stop the car.

I grope for the monkey wrench which is behind Cora's seat.

What are you going to do with that? she says in a frightened voice.

What do you think?

She makes a grab for my arm as I get out of the car. No, she screams. Don't! She says it again as I run across the road, the monkey wrench a dead weight in my hand. I hear his tires screeching around the curve.

It's like my own death. Everything important flashes before my eyes. Not the events of my life—the events of the day. Maybe they are the events of my life. I see the car and Lincoln Rockwell X and the beating and Cora's hidden tits. I see all the blurs and bumps and rising dust of the road. I see myself running scared. All the things I always wanted to do. I see the road stretching to its perspective point, bisected by the flashes of oncoming headlights.

All this at once, as I watch the car round the last curve of the access road and come directly at me. I release the heavy wrench and my arm feels weightless. The wrench shatters the windshield glass, sails on across the side of Allen's head, floats out through the rear side window.

Inches from me the car swerves and heads across the four lanes. Cora screams, but it misses the Mustang, bounces off an abutment, hits another abutment broadside, and stops.

I don't want to look but I do.

His left arm is part of the mangled steering wheel. The

rest of his body is relaxed, leaning slightly forward like someone exhausted from heat. His head rests against the splintered glass of the window. I avoid looking at what the wrench did to the side of his head.

I return to the Mustang. The wheels. Its motor throbs; the whole car shakes. I get in and turn off the ignition.

I touch Cora's arm and she slides away from me.

You dumb fucking shit, she says.

She begins to beat her fists on the scarred leather of the dashboard.

George Alec Effinger wrote his first published story this past summer. Also his fifth or sixth. He has enormous talent and a brilliant future. He introduces this story with: "Gremmage is a weird place. Weird people live there. It has its own mythos, and somehow attracts varied, foreign elements. It's not surprising, then, for Frat-rat to meet the Great Pumpkin there, or Wonder Woman, or . . . or . . . "

Trouble Follows

by Geo. Alec Effinger

I like it there. It really wasn't such a bad town. I grew
up in Oil City, which wasn't that far away, and I could
just see myself staying around the area. I didn't particularly
want to do any traveling. There's plenty of time for that.

I could just see it. I graduate from college, and someone
from Pennco Products is right there, the job and next
month's inventory forms all ready to go. No sweat. I
didn't mind the idea of holding one of those stultifying
little jobs: money is money, and I didn't believe that it
made any difference how you earned it. I could always do
those important and creative things when I came home at
night.

And then there was Carolyn. You knew we were pinned;
there was that unwritten law about waiting until gradua-
tion to make the whole thing legal. Okay, we waited, but
not impatiently. We could see it coming: the adequate
Cape Cod on Lakehurst Drive, our first Craftsman lawn
mower, our first color Zenith, and then our first tricycle on
the lawn. It was all there; it seemed like it was only a few
minutes away.

That was how I was. Who I was, now, I was Joseph M.
Barbieri, Jr. I was a sophomore at Gremmage State College. I was tall and heavy, I wore my blond hair short with
long sideburns so that I could still look hip; I wore faded
blue Gremmage sweatshirts with their sleeves cut off, I
wore white or blue Levis that were shrunken halfway to
my knees except when I cut the legs off altogether and
wore them as shorts; I wore sneakers without socks, except

on dates, when I wore brown penny loafers without socks. I was a good man; I loved it there.

"What a world we live in!" I used to say. I used to marvel like a granny who had just discovered the cartridge pen. "I love you, technology! Science—there's where the money is." I used to say this a lot. "Even if you don't care about money, like I do (that is, I don't really care about money at all, just so that I enjoy what I'm doing), well, science gives you the opportunity to become absorbed into your work, and what more can a man ask? To be thoroughly wedded to one's endeavors, to the exclusion of all else. Where else but in science?"

I was an Elementary Education major, the only male El. Ed. major on campus. I never had any real intention to teach, though; I just didn't have the patience.

Have you begun to see the way I was?

"What sort of a day was it?" I used to ask this a lot, too. It was a rhetorical question, but it referred mostly to the same event. I used to talk about the four-minute mile: why, I could just see Roger Bannister running around that track. I could only have been eight or so at the time, but I remembered it distinctly. And there he was, in Australia or somewhere, and there *I* was, in Oil City, Pennsylvania. Wow. Technology. "A day like all days . . ."

What sort of a day was it? Lousy.

Well, wait a minute. Take a look. See? That cleft in the trees: that's Route 16. That's the way they came. If you had been there that morning you could have seen them coming—a storm; a big, black, ugly storm. And a dirty wino nut.

Thunder rolled: cousins of the Catskill dwarves bowling in the blackest Pennsylvania afternoon. Lightning flickered, nerves of the storm, fire imbedded in the darkness. Do you see the day?

The storm and the wino. The storm found me first. I had had one of those magical afternoon chem labs: zip zam! hydrogen; zip zam! manganese dioxide. I usually skipped them rather than walk all the way out to the Hill. Dr. Seagren was a jerk, anyway. I went to this one because it was the last lab before midterms. I was always prudent; you know I was prudent. I think you mentioned it in a letter once.

When I came out of the chem lab it was already raining. The sky was pitch or coal black, and the rain was coming down so hard that I couldn't see across the street. I was fifteen minutes away from the dorm, so I said screw this and ducked into the Union to wait it out.

I opened the door to the Union. In the gloomy light I saw about fifteen people, all looking toward me. It was always so exciting around there. You used to spend the entire time waiting for someone to come in with The News. Just as I stepped past the threshold a great flash of lightning lit the room brightly. I stood there, wet as a welldigger's kneecap; the rainwater dripped from me onto the floor, making little freshets that danced before me.

"Hey, Barbs," said one of the jocks, "it raining?"

"No," I said, "Kathy What's-her-name's out there that black bikini of hers again. I was staring at her for while and worked up this great sweat." I walked over one of the tables, sprinkling the tessellated floor with rain water. Then I sat down with you; the thunder echoed.

The Union was in the basement of Pinchot Hall. It was really frightening: cinder block wall painted a gay and cheerful white, molded plastic chairs and aluminum tables, hip and groovy travel posters of France and Austria hanging limply. All around the room were the painted wooden crests of the campus frats. "You see, if we give them a place where they can meet each other, informally, where the faculty and the student body can get together over coffee and talk out their differences, why, then, it'll keep them off the streets or something."

Another bolt of lightning, and the basement blossomed with light and died. In the doorway stood a man.

I saw him first. "Oh, for crying out loud," I said.

The man was of late middle age, perhaps about fifty-five. His face was scored with deep creases: either continual and longstanding worry or habitual debauchery. His long gray hair and untrimmed beard made him appear much older than he otherwise might. He was very tall; the pain which drew his brows together so tightly should also have made him lean heavily on his staff. But he did not—he stood very straight, and was easily the tallest person in the Union. His body was thin, actually gaunt. His arms were small but well-muscled; the exposed areas of his skin were burned a dark brown. His clothing was shabby, a few torn and ragged garments that could not protect him from the weather. He was barefoot.

"For crying out loud," I said, "look at the hippy creep!"

Yes, you must see the place and the day. You must see the kind of person I was. And now you must see what happened.

He walked slowly, without the wino hurry of those who don't have anywhere to go. You've seen them, the bums in Washington Square, traveling in wide, swinging arcs from bench to bench. Yeah, well, not this one; he walked slowly, everywhere to go but all the time to get there, too. He heard my comments and glanced at me. He stood by our table but said nothing.

One of you said, "Yeah, fella, cut it off." We laughed, but he stood there, still watching us in silence.

I think I was irritated when one of you asked him to sit down with us. I remember a few times when one of those drunks cornered me and started telling me his sob stories. Being hit for money never annoyed me: you just say "no." But standing there on the street listening to him tell you what a great wife he used to have, and his kids, and how he had all these buddies in the war, and the ~oems he was going to have published . . . all the time ~ ¿~ by the arm, and you meet desperation; soon you know he's going to start with the wrinkled-up snapshots. It always bothered me for a while afterward.

I had better ways to spend that afternoon, even if it was only standing out and getting wetter.

"Look, don't you have somewhere to go?" I asked.

The old man regarded me. Right then I knew that I had made a mistake; I was going to be his target. "I've been traveling a long time, and I have a long way yet to go."

I turned to you, smiling, my hair still clinging wetly to my forehead. "Ah, the cryptic comment. We are fascinated; we insist that you tell us the history of your travels."

"I've wandered for many years. In all that time I have only passed by my home once, and I couldn't recognize it then."

"Wow," said one of you.

"Yes," said the old man.

"Don't tell me," I said, "let me guess. You've left a beautiful wife and a growing boy, and all these years you've been trying to get back to them, but the will of the gods prevents you."

"Yes," said the old man, "that's true. But I know that I won't see my home and family again."

"Well," I said, smiling sarcastically, "it's just a matter of not losing faith."

"Faith. I've learned faith. But still my past life is gone forever."

"That's no way to talk. I'll bet you get home all right, and your beautiful and faithful wife will be waiting, and all the people will cheer, and your son will have grown up strong and handsome."

"There is no chance," he said.

"What's happening?" asked one of you.

I took a drink of your Coke, pausing to look at the old man over the rim of the paper cup, aware of the dramatic pause. I put the cup back on the table and recited:

> " 'Good my lord, you seem to me the Ithacan,
> The cursèd of the gods, that clever king,
> Odysseus; upon those foreign strands
> The fickle poison sea had cast him up.
> He won such favors: those of goddesses
> And mortal scepter'd hands in unknown states,
> Who neither glanced the webbings of his tongue.' '

"Ulysses?" asked one of you.

"Odysseus," I said. "We have here with us in Pinchot Hall, right here in Gremmage, Pennsylvania, right here with us at our table, a famed and veritable mythological character." I turned to the old man. "And we can't tell you how happy we are to have you here with us today. What do you think of our country so far?"

"My name is Ahasuerus," he said, "and I will accept a quarter from you."

"We don't have any change on us," I said.

"Here, what the hell, here's a dollar. Go buy some Thunderbird," said one of you.

"I cannot accept more than a quarter."

"Okay," I said, "you lose."

"I know I've lost, but at least I have hope. It's you that still must make *your* journey."

I pushed my chair away from the table, trying to look disgusted. "I don't know about you guys, but I think my enigma compartment is just about filled. Why don't you just tell us how you would have been a great architect and how much you regret the hurt you've caused those who love you?"

"I have hurt, and I hope to be forgiven. Now it's your job to remember when *you* have hurt, so that you may be forgiven also."

"Well, God damn *you*, old man," I said. "Why don't you just let me take care of myself; I haven't heard any complaints lately."

The man who wanted to be called Ahasuerus rose from

his chair. I could watch him begin to rage: his eyes opened wider, his lips parted, he began to breathe deeply. His hands grasped the staff, and I could see the muscles of his arms quivering. When he spoke, his voice cracked with fury:

"You may leave the cursing to the Lord thy God Whose name you take so lightly. Your ignorance is no defense against His wrath. How many times do you have to be told?"

"Repent, right?" I said. "Why don't you get out of here before the campus cops come and take you away?"

"I have to go. It's my fate to walk; I have to meet you over and over again, and my old sins are always thrown back to me in your words. I can't forget them the way you do, but for me this memory is my only hope."

"Brave Odysseus, go home. Poseidon has been dead these many years, and your wrinkled Penelope waits alone. Get out of here."

The old man turned silently and walked slowly to the door. I watched him go, angry at his pretentious nonsense. I waited for him to turn at the door, I waited for him to address one last, melodramatic line to me. He didn't; he disappeared slowly into the dark hallway.

"That was pretty rotten," one of you said. "I mean, even nuts have feelings, too, you know."

"All right," I said, "why don't you go out and apologize? For crying out loud, who invited him in here in the first place?"

"Hey Barbs, it's okay," you said. "I just always feel sorry for them winos. I mean, don't you think they got enough to worry about?"

"Right. I'm the bad guy. You guys sit here and repent. I'm going to take all this stuff back to the dorm before supper."

I got up and walked to the door. I was surprised to find that the old man was still climbing the stairs, although it had not been all that long since he had left. I came up behind him.

"Don't stop now," I said, impatiently. "Come on, walk faster."

He turned and recognized me. "Once I said the same thing to a man. He had stopped to rest on my doorstep. He said to me, 'I will go, but you must walk until I come again.' That very day I began to follow him, and I haven't seen my home or family since."

"Yeah, and I've got this really tough Chaucer course. It was supposed to be a gut."

"I get this kind of rude reception everywhere I go. It hardly bothers me any more except that I know that you're not listening to what I say."

"Hey, I've got a great idea," I said angrily. "Why don't you just give up and go home? You don't have to take the rudeness, you know. You some kind of masochist? Or the people at home find some objection to your appearance, or what?"

He turned away from me. " 'Blessed are you when men revile you and persecute you and utter all kinds of evil against you falsely on my account.' "

"We all have our cross to bear, right? Well, look, if I can bear mine and go bowling at the same time, you can, too."

" 'If any one among you thinks that he is wise in this age, let him become a fool that he may become wise. For the wisdom of this world is folly with God.' "

"That's about enough. Look, old man," I said, jabbing my hand at his chest, *"fuck off already!"* I tried to push by him on the stairway. He put a hand on my arm to stop me. I heard the anger and restraint in his voice, even though the tone had become calmer. "Come," he said, "join me."

I shook my head and went by. The last I saw him, he was heading away from the campus. The storm was breaking up, and it had stopped raining by the time I got back to the dorm. That evening, in the middle of dinner, I suddenly became restless. I started out after the old man. I really can't understand what happened to him; I should have caught up to him a long time ago.

I've been going a couple of months now. I'm starting to look pretty grungy myself, but I don't want to stop until I find him. I'd really like to start turning back, though: finals are coming.

The Game-Playing Literature

by Frederik Pohl

My late collaborator, Cyril Kornbluth, once wrote a story called *The Only Thing We Learn*. He didn't think it necessary to complete the quotation, or indeed to attribute it. He was, after all, writing for a science-fiction audience. Ess Effers are usually cynics and always time-binders. The message that the only thing to be learned from history is that no one ever learns anything from history is not news to them. In fact, the only quarrel an sf writer or reader might have with the statement would be that it is incomplete, and should properly read: "The only thing we learn from history is that we learn nothing from history—unless we view history, both past and present, as a science-fiction story."

In order to see why this statement is true we must first explain what we mean by a "science-fiction story." This isn't easy, since the defining of the term "science fiction" has never been done in a really satisfactory fashion. Science fiction may be a story about the future, or a story about space travel, or a Japanese monster movie, or a political parable. It may also be none of those things. It may be *about* anything, anything at all, because that quality which most clearly distinguishes sf from non-sf writing has to do not with content but with method.

This is true, of course, not only of science fiction but of its collateral relative science. Most of us rather hastily and thoughtlessly regard "science" as a sort of collection of linear accelerators and space vehicles and organic chemistry models. In fact it is not any of these things; it is only a systematic method of gathering and testing knowledge, involving certain formal procedures: gathering information, forming a theory to explain the information, predicting certain consequences of the theory and performing an experiment to test the prediction. If you investigate any area of knowledge (whether it is stellar physics or the number of angels who can dance on the head of a pin) by this method, you are doing science. If you use any other method, you are doing something else.

In the same way, science fiction has to do with methodology, and "the science-fiction method"* is that quality in the creative process of the science-fiction writer which describes the parameters within which he can speculate. The sf method is parallelistic, universal, and anti-deterministic. If we throw dice and see a six come up, the layman sees only a six; the writer using the sf method sees that a six *has* come up, but that any of five other possibilities *might have* come up.

I do not pretend, of course, that all sf writers consciously view the universe in this way, or even that sf stories do not exist in which this feature is minimal if it exsts at all. What I do think is that it is this feature which gives sf the special qualities which make it more interesting than any other kind of fiction. I think it is what Arthur Clarke meant, for instance, when he said that he wrote sf in preference to other kinds of fiction "because most other literature isn't concerned with reality."

Science fiction makes good propaganda literature, and there have in fact been times when the freedom to think and say unorthodox sentiments was severely repressed outside of science fiction. Probably that is why Jonathan Swift chose (or innovated) the sf form for *Gulliver's Travels;* he could not compare France to England to the disadvantage of England in open terms without running risks to his livelihood, but he could say the same things without fear as long as he used the science-fiction disguises of "Blefuscu" and "Lilliput." In America a decade or two ago, when Joseph McCarthy reduced journalists, academics, and even statesmen to terrified silence, sf magazines went right on talking about anything and everything as though

---

* For the term "the science-fiction method" I am indebted to an English sf writer named John T. Phillifent, more frequently seen under his pen name of John Rackham. I am not sure that he means the same thing by it as I do, but the first use of the term I encountered was in a private communication from him.

the Senate Permanent Investigations Subcommittee had
never existed.

The existence of sf-as-agitprop has obscured the to-my-
mind far more important feature of sf-as-analysis. But it
is the analytical powers of the sf method that make its
effectiveness as propaganda great; an sf story not only
makes a statement about a particular imaginary world but
carries the broad general implication that an infinite number of differing worlds are possible, and that small random
changes in causal factors may produce overwhelming
changes in social structures, kinds of morality, and even
"human nature."

For one example, consider religion. Theologians are
just now beginning to catch up with science-fiction writers
in thinking about the religious implications of possible
non-human life on other planets. Few if any of them have
yet faced the problem of wholly *alien* theologies. Nearly
every human society stipulates One True God, a Heavenly
Father who rewards and punishes. Clearly this is biology-
related; humans have two sexes and a helplessly dependent
infancy, requiring a family structure for survival. But
what would be the theology of a sexless race, or one
hatched from eggs laid and abandoned like the sea turtle's?
Nor has any theologian that I know of approached the
question raised in Brian Aldiss's *The Dark Light-Years*.
Most humans, Aldiss argues, attach sacramental importance
to such biological functions as sex (ritual marriage) and
eating (saying grace at meals, ingestion of bread and wine
at mass, etc.) But why should some other race not attach
equal sacramental importance to such other biological
functions as, for instance, excretion?

It is this systematic investigation of what causal factors
are possible and what social consequences may follow
them that makes science fiction a splendid tool for social
analysis. To be sure, it need not be done exclusively within
the pages of *Analog* or *Amazing Stories*, or even in the
form of a story at all. Think tanks like the RAND Cor-
poration, the Hudson Institute, the Institute for the Future
in Connecticut, Bertrand de Jouvenel's "futuribles" panels
in Paris, and many others do in fact use these techniques
in nonliterary ways. But science fiction taught them all
how, and science fiction is still the most pleasurable way
of doing these things.

In essence science fiction reduces the entire continuum
of human knowledge to a sort of board game, and by
systematically changing the rules of the game one or a

few at a time investigates the possibility of alternate societies. Is this an important thing to do? No, not just important; it is transcendental, for there can be no hope of making a change in any condition we deplore until we know what alternatives are open to us. Science fiction gives us a sort of catalogue of possible worlds. From the wishbook we can pick the ones we want. Without it we can resent and deplore, but our capacity to change is very small.

One of the great personal satisfactions of living in the world of science-fiction readers and writers is observing how game-playing reduces partisan tensions. Our up-tight "real" world affects science fiction, too. Some sf people are right-wingers and some are left; some are deeply religious, some not at all; some battle for women's lib or black power or the freedom of the drug scene and some are firmly for the Establishment; and yet all of them are able to join in the game.

In a real world that every day seems more partisan, more grimy, more sullen, and more violent, this is a source not only of pleasure but of hope. Perhaps The Method can spread. Perhaps the world at large can learn from sf. And perhaps then the ants won't have to replace us after all.

Dave ?elcher is a retired naval officer and surgeon who now vrites for other than the medical journals. I believe this is his first published story, although it is by no means his last. I am proud to be able to include it in this collection.

He writes: "With the ._____ f transplants running, only a fool risks an ac_.a. t. From street to operating room, you are being prepared. Before your X-rays are through the tank, lots are being drawn to apportion the real you. To those who want you to be a part of them. So there are problems."

Just Dead Enough

by C. Davis Belcher

The green Chevrolet was stalled at the corner of Washington and Pine Streets. Behind it, the truck driver felt his patience drain away until, with a curse, he shifted gears and rolled his huge truck backward. The protruding sheets of steel sliced through the Volkswagen behind him and through the head of the driver, John Phillpott Tanker.

The ambulance drivers who brought him in had little hope. The nurses in the Emergency Room had less. The residents struggled on, patching torn blood vessels, giving transfusions, wrapping his head in a new plastic bag, and trying every other trick any one of them could think of before they too admitted it was hopeless.

Walter Sturbridge heard about it Sunday evening when an old friend, an elevator operator at University Hospital, called him on the phone. Sturbridge set a record for the trip in. Trotting down the basement corridors toward the north side of the hospital, he saw old Loomis waiting for him.

"How is he?" Sturbridge said.

"He's messed up pretty bad." Loomis steered him toward his elevator. "Let's take this thing up to three where we can sit and talk a bit." They settled, lit cigarettes. Sturbridge waited.

"What they want, Mr. Sturbridge, is to transplant Mr. Tanker's heart."

Sturbridge slouched down in the oversized red plastic chair that he had pulled into the patch of light from the elevator door. He stared back at Loomis. The deserted hospital office, empty since Friday, still held the lingering smells of the girls who worked here.

"They got this fellow, Rowalski, they're just achin' to put a new heart in. Been in and out of here since high school. Four, five years ago they did a valve job. Worked for a little while," Loomis said, "then went to pieces. These doctors do them transplants have to wait and wait. Sometimes work for days on someone and see them die before they can find what they need. They got maybe a dozen waiting, so they're always looking."

Was he a feature writer, Sturbridge thought, or a stupid cub reporter feeling sorry for himself? So it was a hot night and he had missed the Ed Sullivan Show. This was University Hospital and not the Tankerville *Herald*. When they said, "What can we do for Tanker?" and got back a big fat "Nothing," someone had surely asked, "What can we do with Tanker?" A healthy thirty-two-year-old with his head smashed by a truck. And all Sturbridge could think about was that ten million dollars rated a mighty big funeral. But not the characters in here that looked for wrecks like Tanker.

Old Loomis wandered around the dark office looking for a wastebasket he could spit in. "Shakes you up when it's someone you know," he said. "They ain't heartless, these fellers. Otherwise. Anything they could do for Mr. Tanker they would gladly do. But when it's like this, they get to thinking about the ones needing transplants, and start nagging the office to get permission."

Years of war and newspaper reporting had toughened Sturbridge outwardly, but he remained tenderhearted. Thinking of John Philpott Tanker being cannibalized for spare parts like a wrecked car made him ill. When they had first seen him, they had known this was it. Right away someone had said, "Who owns Tanker? When he's dead, that is." Someone had said, "Get the papers signed so we'll be all set to go." As if Tanker were some casual bit of wreckage.

The elevator buzzed and the big "7" lit up. "They're getting ready up there," Loomis said. "I'll drop you off on six."

The corridors, crowded and endless, overwhelmed him with a dozen different hospital smells as he moved from ward to ward. What rankled in Sturbridge was that Hartman, that old poop of a family lawyer, had glimpsed this and brought along his partners to help with the family, while Sturbridge, the fair-haired boy of the Tankerville

"We're about ready now. We'll really clean house to-night, if they don't fool around too long in Recovery."

"You just have to wait until he dies, don't you?"

"Until he's pronounced dead. Can't say just when the end is."

"How come?"

"Well, when is a man dead—when he stops breathing, or his heart stops beating, or when there's irreversible brain damage, or what? In the old days, no problem. You could just let the body lie around until the neighbors came in with the police. That was when you could let a person get really dead dead, Mr. Sturbridge. But the liver, kidneys, heart, and all that don't wait around. They get dead dead pretty fast, too. You've got to be pretty spry. Not so spry there's any loose talk about murder or manslaughter, but still spry enough so that you have some chance your transplant might take. They have a committee," Gruber added.

Great suffering God, Sturbridge thought, another committee. A committee to decide if you were dead. Not dead dead. Just dead enough.

Loomis came in with coffee. He poised there for a moment like a startled old seagull. "Gotta get back," he said.

"Can you take a minute," Sturbridge asked, "and tell me about Rowalski?"

"Gruber here knows him better. I just see him in the elevator, but Gruber here, his wife and Rowalski's wife, both nurses here one time. About four years ago when he had the valve job done, looked like he was going to be fine, and he and this nurse fall for each other. Nice girl, she was. Got two kids, ain't they?" He looked at Gruber, who nodded. "Sure hope he does well tonight." He tottered off toward his elevator.

Sturbridge lit another cigarette. Gruber didn't smoke. "When does the committee get in on a business like this?"

"Been in close to an hour," Gruber said. "Five of them. They cover everything. All kinds of electrocardiograms and electroencephalograms, and down on the second floor there's a special little lab for tests."

Sturbridge looked at his feet. That was how it was done, he thought. Sitting in the middle of all this data, they were pretty certain just how alive a fellow like Tanker was. The tough part was to decide how little alive Tanker needed to be in order to be dead enough to be legal. Committee members allied with the surgical transplant teams, with millions of dollars in malpractice insurance standing between them and any finger-pointers, might see death come earlier than others.

He looked at Gruber. "You wait until they make up their minds?"

"For the final green light," Gruber said, "but our spies tell us when it's getting close."

"So it's not close now?"

"No. If it was, that little light would be blinking sevens instead of fours. If it started on seven I'd be out of here like a bullet. I'm going back up anyhow, Mr. Sturbridge. Would you like to come up and see a little bit of what getting ready is like?"

Leaving the service elevator, they stepped over a recent litter of empty cartons and bottles. Gruber opened a small door and eased Sturbridge in. The place was like a gigantic airplane cockpit with the odor of intricately processed wire and metal, smelling like nothing else whatever, and he breathed this in like fresh air on a mountaintop. His gaze swept across the precise confusion of this array of dials, lights, meters and gauges, blended into that incredible symmetry possessed only by things that somehow worked. Gruber moved along the panel with a technician's certainty. He pushed a button. "Is everything all right, Miss Lord?" he said.

"Fine, Mr. Gruber, but Dr. Lutz wants the temperature of the liver tank raised one degree."

"O.K., Miss Lord, I'll take care of it."

He was busy for a minute adjusting dials. Then he beckoned. Standing beside him, looking through the plate-glass viewing port, Sturbridge could see the entire operating room. Doctors and nurses, masked, gowned and gloved, stood ready.

The waiting men and women reminded Sturbridge of a painting of communicants at some ancient rite. Here they stood, patiently, many barely out of childhood, with years spent in training, eager to wield the instruments and say the words which are the incantations of their modern magic. Their faith had saved and would save again. In his mind Sturbridge saw other men and women gathered in remote rooms the world over, communing with those powers whose force they respected, waiting, waiting for someone like Tanker. The idea was so overwhelming that his mouth would only say something silly. "What if someone has to take a leak?"

"No problems. Someone is always scrubbing. They go to the john, drink coffee, yak a little, the young ones may get in a little necking, and then they scrub and gown up again. It may go on for hours." He smiled. "You know, my wife was a nurse here, and my brother is one of the doctors out there somewheres. I get it from all sides."

Christ, Sturbridge thought, this transplantation business was how Gruber made a living. He liked it. *I bet the first thing he'll tell his wife will be how he raised the temperature one degree on the liver tank.*

A door slammed on the other side of the partition behind them. "What do you mean visible, you goddamned fool?" a gruff voice said. "That polymyograph they hooked onto him is so damned sensitive, it would give a higher reading hooked onto an old horse turd than it's giving hooked onto Tanker. You scientific hotshots give me a pain in the ass."

There was a pause before a softer, smoother voice replied, "If that boss of yours wasn't so damned anxious to get a new kidney into that worthless son of old man Krillus so he can nick him about twenty thousand, you wouldn't be breathing down all our necks to pronounce this poor devil dead."

"You miserable hypocrite. Would you play God and pass judgment on Krillus' boy just because he had a little tough luck, and deny him a chance to live? We've had both his kidneys out for a week now."

"I'm not hypocrite enough to say this man's dead when a student nurse can look at the dials and see he's alive."

"Dials, my butt. Pull that damn plug out of the wall, and that whole show will stop in two seconds. We've got seven operating rooms ready to go up here, with nurses and doctors killing time playing with each other until you make up your feeble mind this man is dead."

Gruber smiled. He walked along checking the panel, humming happily. "Things always get a little tight in the committee at the end," he said.

Committees were committees, Sturbridge thought. When the high priests of Egypt got together in a back room of the temple, they probably had things to say to each other. He said, "Tell me about Rowalski."

"Good man, always trying. We both studied electronics, and took some courses together. He's a solid technician. After he had the valve job and got married, things looked good for a while and he thought some of getting a job with us here."

"So what does he do?"

"He has a little radio and TV repair shop at home.

Picks up a few dollars but not a living. The agencies help him out."

"Not much of a life," Sturbridge said.

"He lost his gumption after the valve job went bad, and hasn't been the same Rowalski. His wife has the jitters and takes four kinds of tranquilizers and smokes three packs of cigarettes a day. She can't sleep, so things have been going to hell. There's a lot of us wishing him luck tonight."

Sturbridge nodded. "I never thought of it from Rowalski's point of view. Just Tanker's." He rose. "You've been kind," he said, shaking hands, "and thanks, but I better get out of your way now."

Back on Recovery, Sturbridge tried to ____ in and get inside Tanker's room for a quick look, but a nurse spotted him and shooed him away. He sat in a phone booth trying to reach his paper and heard outside, "John, for Christ's sake, old man, we've been set up there for over three hours. Good God Almighty, how long is it going to take you to convince these stupid bastards—" The doctors moved away.

They were working men with a job to do, Sturbridge thought. They knew Tanker's goose was cooked. They had all these cases in here needing transplants, and ever since Tanker was tagged It, they'd been going. Taking blood out of Tanker for matching as fast as they ran it in. How did they know they were matching against Tanker and not some skid-row bum who had swapped his blood for a few dollars? Probably did the best they could. In ancient days they robbed graves so they could study bodies. Now, upstairs, they waited, poised like a suspended shot on television, aiming to cheat death when they started. He was an alien standing there: still he could sense the pressure as it seeped down the stairways and down the elevator shafts and flowed into Recovery.

He yawned. Despite the air conditioning, his clothes were sticky. He needed a shave. Most of all he was tired, tired really of being an onlooker, sneaking peeks through keyholes and unshaded windows.

Perhaps he could see Rowalski, he thought. He dialed the hospital. The central desk said no. Maybe he'd gone up.

Back in the Visitors' Room he found the little light but now it was flashing three. They weren't on top yet, he thought. He went through his coat, tie, shoes and cigarette routine like an enfeebled actor, condemned forever to rehearse an unsatisfactory and misunderstood role. He pulled out a notebook and did the one thing he knew how to do.

He took off his glasses to rub his eyes, lit a fresh cigarette, and felt sorry for himself. The little light was flashing sevens. So now it was close. Upstairs the last cups of coffee were being drunk, last visits to the john were being made, sleepers were being awakened. Around the high sinks it was scrub, scrub, scrub, as each crew's reinforcements moved up, kidding and joking to ease the tension of the hours ahead, like troops, in the last hour before dawn, moving up to the line of battle.

He didn't try to get close to Recovery. Outside Tanker's room three doctors stood in a small, tired, and solemn cluster. Soon there was a fourth. It was 4:15. Sturbridge wondered if all the patients waiting for Tanker were already on seven, or if they were now saying goodbye to their tearful families. Near him an elevator came up and was locked with open door. Aides appeared with long low carts and reels of electric cable.

Then Sturbridge felt a surge of pity and understanding for the fifth man on that committee, who now must be excruciatingly aware that his own squeamishness, conscience, or sense of fitness had condemned him to be the one who finally said Tanker was dead enough. Sturbridge could picture him dragging himself from one dial to another, staring at one group of flashing lights and then another, hoping to find there some mechanistic magic that would relieve him of his burden. For he must know full well that by now University Hospital waited on him.

Sturbridge saw him come out. Hours earlier, he must have been called from a dinner party. Now in his disheveled suit he resembled a sad and bedraggled penguin. He stepped toward the other four and with an oddly appealing gesture threw up his hands.

The long low carts, the reels of cable, more doctors, more nurses, moved into Tanker's room and soon, as if moved by a will of his own, Tanker's bed appeared, still covered and surrounded by tubes and needles, tanks and flashing lights. It moved, in what seemed to Sturbridge a poignantly solemn procession, past the tormented five and into the waiting elevator. The door closed.

Sturbridge heard the nurse. "Desk," she said, "this is Recovery. Patient John Phillpott Tanker expired four thirty-seven A.M."

Sturbridge called his paper and gave them the time of

death. Driving through the early dawn, he thought it would be nice to get home where he could take off his clothes and be comfortable.

When he had typed about half a page, the smell of frying bacon overwhelmed him. God, he hadn't realized he was that hungry. As he ate, he told Maisie all about it. Then he fell asleep over the typewriter. Maisie let him doze a little while, then woke him and he finished the piece. He called it "The Night John Phillpott Tanker Died," and Maisie took it down to the paper while he went to bed.

Even Lawrence Jennings went out of his way to flatter him. "They keep telephoning, Walter. They like it. We need some more. Can you keep them coming?"

Gruber's brother, other doctors, and a lawyer friend coached him. He explained the problems so the ordinary man could see them. He called his second article "Legal Death." Letters poured in screaming, "A man is dead when he's dead and any fool knows that." Others showed more understanding.

He visited families made wretched by their burdens· invalids who neither died nor recovered nor ʳ⁻ ⁻ ᵘ. Instead they lived with the hopes and monst ᵘespairs of the near-dead, bound to life by an umᵇⁱ·ᶜal cord woven by modern science. He knew these fᵃᵐilies well. He wrote and wrote, and called it "The Hopeful Supplicants."

All supplicants might not be equally deserving. In Gruber's control room, the night Tanker died, he had heard the name Krillus. Faintly he recalled a scandal, but could not pin it down. One of the regular reporters, Hank Coggins, filled him in.

"That boy Krillus is a completely no-good son of a bitch. Not just raping three teenage girls and killing two people with his car. Let's face it, some kids are pretty wild. A young boy, full of piss and vinegar, he can do a lot of tough things, but eventually, if he grows up a decent sort of man, people forgive him. But this Krillus boy, Tony they call him, he's just a mean bastard. Always has been. Gutted cats. Beat up small kids. His daddy's money bought him out of everything. But he got sick and ended up with lousy kidneys. They got infected, and a week or so before Tanker died they either had to take his kidneys out or he was going to die. And they took them out."

Sturbridge nodded. "I've seen the artificial kidney machine they used to keep him alive until Tanker showed up."

"That right? Well, Krillus only had this one boy. His

wife's dead years now. He's just a contemptible old fart himself, no self-respecting doctor would put his kidney in anything but a dirty pickle jar, and anyhow he's too old and they had to wait." Hank paused to light a cigarette. "Early that morning when Tanker died, they put one of his kidneys in Tony Krillus and it just worked fine. He takes medicine and some kind of treatment, but three weeks after they put it in, he was running around like you and me and has been ever since."

Sturbridge tried to interview Rowalski, who was doing well, but the hospital would permit no visitors. He drove out one day to see Rowalski's wife. The heat wave had broken; there had been rain and the trees and fields were green. Rowalski's lawn was a litter of bottles, papers, old tires, discarded plastic toys, and a broken cart struggling valiantly to hide the rampant weeds. The iron gate hung awry from a broken hinge. Beyond the cracked and pitted concrete, the porch door stood ajar.

To the left a bench, some tools, and a few disemboweled and dust-covered television sets marked the limits of what had once been Rowalski's shop. A battered baby carriage, a cot, a small basket filled with apples, another filled with tomatoes now intruded on these. On the cot a huge yellow tiger cat flashed green eyes filled with suspicion at Sturbridge, but collapsed into purrs when petted.

He heard the house door open, and turned. The cat repaid this neglect by sinking two large claws into his hand. He made his peace and introduced himself. There were no chairs, so he sat with the cat. Mrs. Rowalski brought out the baby which she put in the carriage, a small child which she sat on the porch, a coffee percolator and the necessary things, a bottle for the baby, cigarettes, and finally a camp stool for herself. She was only about twenty-five, he thought, but he could see how the grinding years had etched her face. They sat there enjoying their smoke, the nice afternoon, the quiet children, and waited for the coffee.

Her hair was brushed back and tied with a piece of candy-box ribbon. She was clean but unadorned. He asked her about her childhood.

Her pregnant mother had fled Germany while the rest of the family were on the way to the gas chambers, and died in Brooklyn of tuberculosis when the little girl was four. From orphanage to foster home to foster home had been the child's dreary round until she became a student nurse at University Hospital.

Her cheerless childhood had left her dull in social situations. She could not joke or flirt easily. Unlike the other student nurses, she had not flexed her emotions by falling in love with at least two medical students, interns, residents, laboratory technicians, elevator operators, or personable male patients.

When Sidney Rowalski was admitted for repair of a defective heart valve, her needs and his met. Their marriage was a monument testifying that he and she had made it. If the valve job had held up, they would have done as well as most.

She checked the baby, then brought out a glass of milk and a cookie for the little girl.

"How do you feel about things now?" he asked her.

She looked at him seriously. He could see the fatigue lines around her eyes and lips. "I can't be sure," she said. "If I could just believe we could be happy."

"And can't you believe this?" he asked.

"I don't know," she said.

On the way home he stopped at the chain drug store. Bill would be coming home from military school this weekend; he bought a box of peanut brittle. Then he went to the corner where the old man sold flowers, and bought a big bunch of yellow roses. Maisie would feel faintly jealous and suspect him of patting some secretary at the Tankerville *Herald*. He couldn't help that.

Publication of "The Hopeful Supplicants" changed Sturbridge's life. Lawrence Jennings stopped him in the hall to pound him on the back and say, "Man, you can really write." The lawyer, Hartman, stopped him on the street, took him to lunch, and talked and talked about how much he and his wife had enjoyed the articles. Things were looking up, Sturbridge thought; at least it didn't look as if he had to worry about his job. Then UPI asked to syndicate his articles. At last, Sturbridge admitted, he could taste money, he could smell money, and, God willing, he would damn soon have some.

He was working hard on his fourth article, which he called "By These Hands." He hoped to convey something of what he had glimpsed through the window in Gruber's control room the night Tanker died. And the things Gruber and his brother had told him since. At the Hartmans' for dinner, the Sturbridges met a nurse from University Hospital, Gladys Peterson, an old friend of Mrs. Hartman's. "Mr. Sturbridge needs your help, Gladys," Mrs. Hartman said. "He needs to know just what went on."

Gladys took a big swallow of her bourbon and started in. She was a big blond blustery sort of girl, good-natured and willing. She had an eye for what counted. She took Sturbridge through the developing drama of the operating floor as the patients came up. She followed them as they were moved to different rooms and told him what the rooms contained. With the arrival of the body of John Phillpott Tanker, the overall show faded out, because she was in the room where the heart transplant from Tanker to Rowalski was being done.

"A thing like that is real exciting, Mr. Sturbridge. I mean even when you've worked around hospitals for years like I have, still there's something about putting another heart in a person that makes the shivers run up my spine. I'm just not tough enough, I guess." She paused for a swallow of her bourbon, a quick fluff fluff to her hair, a glance around to see that she was holding her audience.

"They had Rowalski up in the operating room for, oh, a good hour or more before Mr. Tanker finally died. They were checking up all the time back and forth with Recovery, because they had to get Rowalski connected to the heart-lung machine in plenty of time, but yet not too early because it don't do them any good to be on one of those heart-lung machines a minute longer than they need to." She finished her bourbon and Mrs. Hartman brought her another. Gladys took a good swallow. "I tell you, Mrs. Hartman, I just couldn't be a scrub nurse today. I just couldn't stay with it. When I was a scrub nurse, just one doctor did the operating and the other doctors helped him by keeping things back out of the way so he could see what he was doing. And if they started in trying to do any of the operating, they got a good sharp rap on the fingers from the doctor that was doing it. But it's not like that now. What with hooking up the heart-lung machine and maybe doing a tracheotomy, that's putting a tube in their neck to hook up to the anesthesia machine, and then opening them up so you can get at the liver or kidney or heart or whatever you are going to transplant, why you may have three or four people cutting and sewing at the same time. There is so much to do and it goes fast, fast, fast, and the girls that are scrubbed just have to be quick and pay real strict attention, because when those young squirts stick out their hand for something they want it right now. A nurse may have been out necking with that same doctor the night before, but she better be right on her toes in that operating room. She won't be out necking with that doctor and she won't be in there giving him the wrong instruments, either, if she can't stay with it.

"You know, Mr. Sturbridge, the really spooky part for me was when they had taken Rowalski's heart out but they hadn't put Mr. Tanker's heart in yet. That's when you really looked at that heart-lung machine over there with the blood running down through the big cellophane bag and the oxygen bubbling up through it. You can hear the pumps going chunk-chunk-chunk-chunk, and see the blood flow into those plastic hoses that run from the machine down across the floor to Mr. Rowalski. Then they take Mr. Tanker's heart out of the perfuser and they have it up there trimming it so it will fit exactly and you know I wanted to holler at those pumps—don't stop—don't stop— don't stop—because you could just see that that pump was all there was."

"By These Hands" was reprinted across the country, and Sturbridge had the rare and delightful pleasure of seeing and hearing himself quoted. When *Readers' Digest* wrote requesting reprint rights, he found that even the fullest cup could hold a little more. Sturbridge's style had appeal. UPI asked him to write a column, once a week to start, on transplant problems. UPI felt it might go if he wanted to give it a try.

His concern for Rowalski's family was genuine. Lawrence Jennings agreed to give plenty of publicity to any local groups that would help out, and between the veterans' organizations, the lodges, the churches, and Rotary, they made a howling success of cleaning up and painting the place. The Legion rearranged its car lottery so that Mrs. Rowalski, with everyone forewarned, got one of the cars. Rowalski, doing well, was being considered for a trial visit home.

Later that week the reporter, Hank Coggins, came up. "That Krillus boy ain't changed none. Killed another kid this morning with his damned car."

"What happened?"

"He hit a kid named Andrews. Family lives down by the brick kilns. Killed him instantly."

The next day Hank was back. "There's more to that story if you want it."

"Dump your bag," Sturbridge said.

"It's a mixed-up deal. Tony Krillus had a row with his old man and moved in with a friend in the old Packer Apartments down by the railroad station. Usually if a

family has money, there isn't too much trouble about killing a kid down in that neighborhood. But this time old
man Krillus wasn't having any. Seems Tony had his own
car and he's over twenty-one and the old man either can-
celed the insurance or it run out, so there isn't anything
to pay the Andrews family with. So the family got a lawyer,
that new fellow, Yates, and he's had Tony Krillus arrested
until he posts bond. Yates swears somebody is going to
pay."

Sturbridge wrote a column on the hazards of keeping
criminals or insane people alive by transplants. The liver
transplant died, and he did a little more work on his fifth
big article, which he called "On Borrowed Time." Then
one day he saw Hartman boil up the stairs as if outrunning
a subpoena server and duck into Lawrence Jennings' office.
A few minutes later Sturbridge's phone rang and Jennings
asked him to come over.

Jennings' face was flushed, his lips tightly pursed.
"Walter," he said, "you're the nearest thing to an expert
we've got around here on this transplant business. Have
you ever heard anyone argue against declaring a man dead
because his kidney or heart was still alive in someone else?"

Sturbridge stared at him. "Well, no. The early transplants were kidneys taken from identical twins, and the
question didn't come up. When they started doing hearts
and lungs and more and more kidneys, they had to use
organs from people who were legally dead, but they had to
work fast. Of course all kinds of releases are signed, but
I've never heard of any legal tangle about it."

"I told you so," Hartman cried, jumping up and waving
his hands at Jennings. "John Philpott Tanker was legally
dead. Five doctors at University Hospital said so. No
whiz-kid lawyer can change that."

"Is that so?" said Jennings. "Well, how about the fellows who were hung by the neck until some doctor said
they were dead, but the relatives took them down and revived them; how about the ones that came to in an undertaker's shop after some trusty sawbones said all was over;
do they have to stay legally dead? Hell, no. You know that
and I know that."

"The whole body was revived," Hartman cried. "The
same person was still there. The doctor's mistake was obvious."

"Does it have to be the whole body?" Jennings demanded.

"How about filling me in?" Sturbridge said. "I can hear the shooting but what are you shooting at?"

"It's the damnedest thing," Jennings said. "You know about Tony Krillus. Well, Yates is determined to get money. Old man Krillus won't part with any. Holly here— he pointed at Hartman—is in Probate Court starting on John's estate. Yates has brought in this New York fellow, and Holly can't even get the death certificate admitted. They argue that it is an inaccurate and unsatisfactory statement inasmuch as Tanker just isn't totally dead."

Hartman snorted. "I never expected in all my days to sit in a courtroom and hear it argued that a man wasn't totally dead when he's been out in Spring Valley for months with a big marble stone on top of him. I feel like I'm watching one of those way-out television shows."

"Damn it all, Holly," Jennings said, "transplanting hearts and kidneys was way-out television just a damned short while ago. I don't want any calm superior legal air about this. This is my ass. I expect to inherit a damn big chunk of John's estate as you both well know. Anything, and I mean anything, God damn it, that threatens to get in my way is a matter of deep personal concern."

There was a pause.

"What does Yates hope to gain with all this hoopla about the death certificate?" Sturbridge asked.

"Now you're getting to the nub of it," Jennings said. "My spies tell me that Yates has dreamed up the idea of filing suit against the Tanker estate. He is going to claim that without Tanker's kidney Tony Krillus would be dead. So what Yates is going to say is that if Tony Krillus killed the Andrews boy, he did it only because Tanker's kidney kept him alive to do it. So he is going to sue the hell out of Tanker. So what I am asking Holly is, does the whole body have to be revived? I'm worried as hell about this. A man can lose an arm or a leg or even both arms and both legs and his eyes and the Lord knows what else and still be John B. Citizen. But can a kidney or a heart lose everything else and keep on living and be John B. Anybody? Or just what the hell is the situation?"

Sturbridge couldn't take his eyes off Hartman. *God,* he thought, *he's really got the wind up.* He watched a muscle jump in Hartman's cheek beneath the handkerchief he was rubbing over his face.

Hartman cleared his throat and got a grip on himself. "I think you are getting excited without good reason, Lawrence. Judge Cotton has to let them present whatever

bench: the dank audienc~ ~ondemned to limbo, picked
their noses, loosened their tie~, and squirmed in the eternal
human effort to fit a hard bottom to a hard oak seat.

Then another sigh. The lawyers and clerks had been
driven back. The judge was alone. Silence fell.

"I find in the case before us," he said, in a voice as dry
and serene as the whispering of leaves in the early morning,
"that the recipients of tissue transplants from John Phillpott
Tanker should share with the legitimate heirs in the distri-
bution of his estate. They cannot replace these heirs but
they cannot be excluded. The degree of sharing will be
determined by future argument before this court."

Jennings looked at Sturbridge and sighed with relief. "I
was scared, Walter, that he might leave the family out entirely. This I can live with. We'll have to work out a settlement because none of us will want to wait forever. I have
to call my wife."

That night Sturbridge watched Sidney Rowalski on television. Rowalski was asked about the lawsuit. "After all,"
he said, "God knows, I'm grateful I got Mr. Tanker's heart.
I'd be dead probably if I hadn't, because I couldn't have
hung on much longer. I had rheumatic fever when I was
a boy and what heart I had left was going to pieces. But
still I feel queer. Part of me is really Mr. Tanker and most
of the rest of Mr. Tanker is gone. It's different somehow
from having a plastic or a metal heart, I th~ ~k. I never had
one, but you could imagine it being par of yourself, like
glasses, or false teeth. But my heart be~ ~ngs to Tanker and
I'm not trying to be funny."

Later he was asked about the money. "Well, I'm glad,"
Rowalski said. "At first, I admit I had a funny feeling I
was being ungrateful somehow and that just getting Mr.
Tanker's heart should be enough. My wife argued with me,
pointing out that although I felt pretty good right now I
had no way of telling what lay ahead. And then there was
the children. If I was going to keep myself going I had to
take care of Mr. Tanker's heart, and if Mr. Tanker's heart
was going to keep going it had to take care of me. We
were both in me together. I never knew Mr. Tanker, but I
finally decided he would want his heart and me mighty
well taken care of."

Right on the heels of his column on the court decision,
Sturbridge was notified he had won the Pulitzer Prize.
Lawrence Jennings told him at work, sent out for sand-
wiches and coffee for everyone, and gave Sturbridge a
cold glass of beer. Sturbridge called Maisie and she cried.

There at the paper everyone came up to his office and it was a nice party.

He went home and petted Maisie until she stopped crying. Bill had gone AWOL from military school and thumbed his way home. The afternoon paper carried Sturbridge's picture and then people started coming. Everybody. Bringing food, bringing liquor, bringing good wishes. They came from the hospital led by the Grubers, from the paper led by Lawrence Jennings, and from the town led by the Hartmans. Sturbridge was completely and utterly satisfied. It was three in the morning before they were gone. He was in a tremendous glow. He could hear Maisie reclaiming her kitchen, which the other women had taken over for the evening. Bill was trying to finish one last piece of chocolate cake. Sturbridge looked at him with great affection.

"You know, Bill," he said, "if you put a heart and a lung, and a kidney and a liver there on the table I doubt if I could tell them apart. But I'm mighty grateful to them, yes sir, mighty grateful. They sure did all right by me." He pulled himself up and started for the stairs.

Maisie called from the kitchen, "I'll be right up, dear."

"You better be," Sturbridge said.

And Bill laughed as only a sixteen-year-old can laugh.

Ed Bryant again. Of this short sketch he writes: "Somebody with an English doctorate once called this story 'an example of nonobjective art,' whatever that is. It may very well be. I originally wrote it as a gift for my dearest friend. It is a love letter."

Right on. But I stil say it is an interesting example of nonobjective art.

Sending
the Very Best

by Ed Bryant

The year of massive starvations and dying diatoms had scarcely begun when I acutely felt the absence of my lover. I determined to send her a greeting card. Thus I found myself in the appropriate little shop on Wilshire, the "Hallmark" emblem conspicuously blazoned above the door.

"May I help you, sir?" The clerk hovered just beyond my seeing. His tone was deferential.

"A card, please."

"For a specific occasion, sir?"

I explained.

"Very good. This way, please."

We stood before the black-enameled wire racks.

"Moving holographic projections, sir. Sixteen-track stereophonic sound. Full sensory stimulation. Infinite replay."

"Impressive," I said. "Your best line?"

"Only the best, sir."

I reached out tentatively, to touch.

"Perhaps if you examined the scenario," the clerk said, handing me

A EULITANY: The Less-than-Aeolian Harper

High on the side of the mountain

The caldron of morning boils up behind the trees. Sun fuzzes the stranger's silhouette as he enters the clearing. He approaches the old man cutting words into the granite block and steps into his attention.

High on the side of the mountain a horse whickers

"Is she buried here?" the stranger asks.

"No," answers the old man from above his asymmetric white beard. "You might call this a cenotaph. Inyan Cara, like any good volcano, was consumed by fire. She is ash riding the wind; perhaps filtering down unannounced over Ireland, or maybe Greece."

High on the side of the mountain a horse whickers, then vanishes

"Ireland." The stranger considers it. "Greece. She'll not be back?"

"No, not unless we try to prevent her returning."

High on the side of the mountain a horse whickers, then vanishes into the timber

"You remember her well?" the stranger asks.

"I remember." The sculptor's dim eyes lose focus. "How she loved to dance and swim. Yes, she loved—"

"Yes," says the stranger, smiling crookedly.

High on the side of the mountain a horse whickers, then vanishes into the timber; the sound

The stranger laughs at the aged sculptor, but his amusement is gentle. "You are less than original, old man." He pauses. "But you do steal from impeccable sources." The stranger says reflectively, "I steal too." He sighs. "So many times I helped pick thorns from her flesh."

High on the side of the mountain a horse whickers, then vanishes into the timber; the sound, spectral echo

The old man continues to chip at the rock as the stranger talks:

"I once glutted the air about her with compliments. Then I realized my error was constant underestimation."

High on the side of the mountain a horse whickers, then vanishes into the timber; the sound, spectral echo, gallops away

"There." The old man wearily sets down his chisel. The inscription is complete:

God's Lioness

The voice comes from everywhere and nowhere and it makes both the stranger and the old sculptor smile.

"I am *not* a fucking cat!"

High on the side of the mountain a horse whickers, then vanishes into the timber; the sound, spectral echo, gallops away on the wind.

"I'll take it," I said to the salesman.

Charting Utopia

by Damon Knight

This chart is intended to show the curiously regular ups
and downs of magazine science fiction in this country since
1926, the year when Hugo Gernsback founded *Amazing
Stories*. The solid line represents the number of new writers
who later became well known. You can see, for instance,
that in 1929 eleven such writers were published for the
first time, and in 1930 twenty-four. The broken line represents the number of sf magazines devoted to original
stories. (Here and there, particularly at the end of the
chart, I include several things that are not strictly magazines—Frederik Pohl's *Star*, my own *Orbit*, Harry Harri-
son's *Nova*, Robert Hoskins' *Infinity*, Samuel and Marilyn
Delany's *Quark*. Except for these, data are taken from the
Index to the Science Fiction Magazines, 1926-1950, com-
piled by Donald B. Day, and the *MIT Science Fiction
Society's Index to the S-F Magazines, 1951-1965*, com-
piled by Erwin S. Strauss.)

It has often been remarked that science fiction has a
ten-year cycle, and you can see now that it is true, more
or less. The new writers' curve peaks at intervals of eleven
and ten years, the magazine curve at intervals of eleven
and twelve years. After 1953 the pattern breaks down; the
expected peaks in the mid-sixties are absent. The slight
upturn at the end of the chart is due to the quasi-magazines
I mentioned before.

The question is, why these booms and busts? I have been
worrying away at the problem off and on for twenty years.
(I am not agile but I am tenacious.)

Let's suppose that the number of magazines is controlled

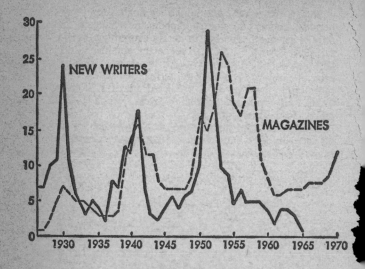

by economic factors (which are known to vary cyclically) and that the number of new writers is a function of the number of magazines—a simple matter of supply and demand. This hypothesis looks pretty good at the beginning of the chart—the huge peak at 1930 can be seen as oversupply, and the subsequent drop brings the two curves together. But what about the jump in the number of new writers, in 1937, that precedes the increase in the number of magazines? And what about the two high points in the magazine curve in 1953 and '57-58, when the writers' curve is falling?

Well, then, let's say that the market can support only a small number of writers, old and new. When a lot of new writers get into print, they are filling vacancies, and when the vacancies are filled there is no more room for new writers, no matter how good they may be. This might be called the clique hypothesis. Editors universally deny that any such thing happens. They say there have always been mediocre writers who would be displaced instantly if anybody better came along.

In fact, the quality of science fiction rises dramatically in periods when large numbers of new writers are entering the field. These periods have always been brief, and in the following years, even though the market may be booming, quality always drops.

Shall we say that even though we don't know why these periodic booms and slumps happen, they happen, and not only in science fiction but in nearly everything else we can measure, from the stock market to the abundance of mice, and that nobody knows why? All this is true, and, in fact, each of the three peaks of the writers' curve on our chart falls within a year of a predicted maximum of A. L. Tchijevsky's human excitability cycle, which in turn is related to the sunspot cycle.

Even if we grant this, it does not follow that we have to lie here and let it happen. If we know an undesired event is coming, we can take steps to ameliorate it, if not prevent it.

In the early forties, and again in the fifties, there was a plague of bad sf magazines. Most of them were short-lived, and no wonder. They were shoestring productions, often edited by people who knew little and cared less about the field, and they increased the market for hackwork, not for the first stories of promising new writers. But even leaving them out of account, why didn't the established sf magazines continue to attract good new writers?

Shall we speculate that there is some kind of resonance effect at work? Let's say that one boom in sf occurs by chance; then each subsequent boom is the result of the one before it—perhaps because each boom impresses a large number of people, who then take about ten or eleven years to train themselves and become professional sf writers. I find this implausible because of the precise timing it requires, and because a new writer who is only eighteen or nineteen is probably too young to have been influenced by sf magazines published eleven years before. C. M. Kornbluth, for instance, would have had to read Harry Bates' *Astounding* when he was seven.

Look at the chart once more. I mentioned Harry Bates: he founded *Astounding* in 1930. John W. Campbell took over that magazine in 1937. In late 1949 Anthony Boucher and J. Francis McComas founded *The Magazine of Fantasy and Science Fiction,* and in 1950 H. L. Gold started *Galaxy.* Well, you say, this makes the problem absurdly simple: these strong editors aroused great enthusiasm, and good new writers poured into the field. Yes, but why did they stop pouring in?

I think all the factors I have mentioned have something to do with the answer. The market is subject to the law of supply and demand. There are cliques, even though editors deny it, and there is a limit to the number of writers a given number of magazines can support. There are cycles in human affairs which have not been explained. There surely is a resonance effect at work, if only because when we have been down awhile we expect to go up. And there are still other factors. Here is one:

Each of the editors I mentioned brought to this field an idea which seemed revolutionary at the time and perfectly obvious later. Bates: Science fiction can have exciting plots and colorful characters. Campbell: Sf can make the future plausible by linking it to the present. Gold: It can dare to be flippant about tomorrow. Boucher/McComas: It can be gracefully written.

Now it seems to me that each of these ideas represents only one aspect of a large and obvious idea: That science fiction can be "serious"—it need not be a subliterary genre but can be as good as its writers are able to make it.

I have a strong conviction that those sharp rises in the writers' curve represent the "Aha!" reaction, and that the drops that follow stand for "Oh, hell." A boom in this field takes place when writers think they see a limitless new territory opening up; it collapses when they find out they were mistaken.

To clean up one loose end, I don't believe any more that writing talent is rare. One reason I don't think so is what I've seen at Clarion; another is that in the last seven years Kate and I have lived in three communities that are hard to find on maps, viz. Milford, Pa., Fairdale, Ky., and Madeira Beach, Fla., and in or near each one we have discovered someone on the very point of becoming a professional sf writer. In Kentucky it was a woman who lived next door; in Florida it was a young man who lived within a block of the place where we held the Milford Conference that year.

Now, therefore, I propose that the supply of good new writers ought to be kept up by any means that come to hand, because when they are plentiful our field is healthy and we all prosper. I suggest that one way to do this is to give over butting our heads at the ends of tunnels. Many an editor in the past has known better than this, but often he is the captive of a publisher who knows what the public likes; and so he goes on, boring fewer and fewer people until his readership drops below the point of no return. Others have been doctrinaires and riders of hobbyhorses.

Another way to accomplish this aim, I find, is to hold

workshops like the Clarion Writers' Workshop in Fantasy and Science Fiction. Traditionally the magazines have been the only place to train new sf writers; we now know there can be other places and other ways.

The chart with which we began does not show it, but we are in another boom now. The writers' curve goes only to 1965, because beyond that point data are hard to get and even harder to evaluate. We won't know for another five or ten years, maybe, which of the new writers are building large reputations now. But I point out that this volume contains the work of sixteen new science fiction writers. Which ones will still be around in 1975 I don't know. There are some I am putting my money on.

Herewith another Effinger—In this story he executes a perfect literary setpiece, as perfect as a *pas de chat* at the Bolshoi. Swift did it in a *Voyage to Laputa;* Goldsmith did it in his *Letters from a Citizen of the World*. Effinger gives us the supreme gift of the satirist, the gift Burns invoked in:

O wad some Pow'r the giftie gie us
To see oursels as others see us!

A Free Pass
to the Carnival

by Geo. Alec Effinger

The restaurant was crowded, even though it was well past the usual mealtime, and some human customers were already beginning to arrive. The lords pushed back the black iron chairs and found their way out through the tables on the patio. A tour of the Village was included in the price of their dinner.

Traffic was heavy on Fifth Avenue. The lords boarded the chartreuse bus, filling about half the available seats. Most of them carried cameras, for their stay on Earth never exceeded three months; the lords were enthusiastic souvenir hunters. The straps of the cameras crisscrossed their naked bodies, dividing them into unequal portions.

Tossin shared a seat with his eggfather near the front of the bus. Behind him his spermfather and his mother also shared a seat. Tossin was a young adult, although his three parents treated him as if he were much younger; he was their only child. He thought New York was very exciting and not at all embarrassing, as did his mother, who resented the crassness of the humans. Tossin rode with his left arm hanging from the window; when he looked down at the street he could see that the shade of his pale-blue skin clashed unpleasantly with that of the chartreuse bus.

They rode through the narrow streets. They churned the stagnating pond of people, leaving behind a short, clear wake which soon refilled with milling humans. Among the pedestrians were very few lords. From time to time a human guide at the front of the bus announced that they were passing a place of interest, or the site of a former

111

famous attraction. As a rule the lords did not know the significance of these places, or they could not decide which of the many cramped buildings was meant, and they took few pictures. The human streets were not worth shooting (they were actually ugly), and the notoriety was impossible to capture. After thirty minutes the bus returned them to the restaurant. It was warm and humid, and their heads were beginning to ache.

Their cab was waiting for them, its human driver obviously impatient and staring at the silent meter. The four lords climbed into the car; Tossin noticed the dismay of the cabbie, who surely expected to be dismissed to find human and paying fares. They drove crosstown along West Ninth. The evening deepened; uptown, floodlights kindled the upper stories of the Empire State Building, and lit the great clouds of haze that surged by. At Sixth Avenue the lords left the car and discharged the cabbie, who thanked them hourly.

They walked down town along Sixth Avenue, strolling from store to store. Tossin pretended not to notice the confusion they caused among the humans. Occasionally the mother made a purchase; at these times she returned money for the articles she chose to take, because the parents' duties were ending and the family was soon to return home. When the articles or the service pleased her she added a generous overpayment.

Tossin stood with his eggfather while they waited for the mother to choose some earrings as gifts for friends at home. Attractive, hand-made jewelry was difficult to find. Tossin asked his eggfather what was taking so long (he fingered the strings of beads impatiently, he jangled bells on chains). "I've been told that these humans have warehouses full of rubbish," he replied. "They live by trying to sell more of it to their fellows than they must accept themselves. They will attempt to fool us into thinking it is genuine; human craftsmen are rare, their products are hidden away."

The eggfather stood beside him, restlessly watching the pointless traffic outside. The boy studied the shifting and resettling motions of his eggfather's body: the movements were mirrored across the shop by his spermfather. Their physiques were nearly identical—his eggfather's muscular arms as covered with the dark hair as his spermfather's, his spermfather's chest as deep and broad as his eggfather's, their penises nestled each in its own mat of dark hair. Tossin reached to touch the smooth skin of his eggfather's shoulder: how perfect it was, even here under the fluorescents. The pink skin of the humans showed every sign of the buried sicknesses they carried. Even in the best light the humans revealed only small uncovered and flawed areas, and under artificial light they became mottled pale and flush. The mother often remarked on this effect, and Tossin noted it now with new understanding.

The family left the store, walking east on West Third Street. Tossin walked quietly for a short time, observing the humans and their reactions. Before he arrived on Earth he had had no clear idea of normal human behavior. Even after his first few weeks of the visit he hadn't yet realized what made the humans so offensive. His spermfather had quoted to him the theory that human vulgarity was a racial characteristic.

Tossin held his arm close to his body, the fingers of his left hand tucked under his right arm, his right hand holding his left elbow. He thought as he walked, and he had no idea that he was forming his adult conceptions.

"Why are humans so obnoxious, then?" he asked.

"Our best scholars say that it's their sex," said his eggfather. "It is well known that a human refers to the other sex as 'opposite.' He can expect sexual attention from only half of the total population. Humans frequently live out their lives in perpetual sexual frustration, so it shouldn't be surprising that it is sublimated into all areas of life: political, economic, and religious, as well as social."

On MacDougal Street the lords found more of the same sort of shops. There was no greater variety; the store windows fought among themselves with weapons of leather, wax paper, burned and smoking grease, cotton and corduroy: articles reproduced without affection in grimy combinations. Tourists crowded the lamplit walks; but whatever of the past's licentiousness remained, leering in the spinning, drug-dark doorways, rode on tourists' shoulders and was left under the Arch when they turned uptown. Tossin could not decide why one store seemed crowded with curious, fingering humans and another stood empty, its last customers apparently exhaled hours before.

As the shops grew more insistent the lords found less of interest. The candles and clothing and jewelry were so obviously worthless. Tossin became aware of how little of the merchandise was acceptable. "Why would they allow these things to represent their own taste and craft?" he asked his eggfather.

"They have no taste, Tossin. When our people first arrived, we found an exciting and vibrant culture, in some ways the rival of our own. But the sense of racial inferiority has proven deadly. Nothing original can be expected from humans as long as competing with our standard of living is the major interest. Humans stupidly feel that mining their cultural heritage is in itself a valid creative act; as long as something old and beautiful remains they are in no trouble. But look around: little is left, little is left."

A tired young man watched the group of lords. Tossin looked at him with less of his former interest in humans, and more of his newly found scorn. The human's long hair was pulled tightly back and tied behind his head. Untrimmed and full, his beard hid his face; his expressions were fleeting approximations of emotion. His body covering were busy layers of fringe and drapings. He gleamed from little eyes of buttons, studs, rivets, buckles. His voice scratched as the lords approached, he spoke to them without hope.

"Come on in off the sidewalk! Why beat your feet on the hot concrete, feeling lowdown, mean, and mungy? Come on into Ted Salomon's Four Seasons, the Village's first and last original basket house. No admission, no minimum, no cover charge. Women and servicemen served half price. Continuous live entertainment: folk, folk rock, and blues." He stopped.

"Come on in. Don't go home to your mother-in-law: you know what she'll do to you." He stopped again. He had no more to say.

The lords looked at him silently. There was disrespect in his words, and ignorance, but the human could not be punished for his people's foolishness. The family had been warned about such traps as the Four Seasons: dishonest drinks of fruit juices and rum extract, little entertainment, and, for the human tourists, inflated prices and the mandatory "tip."

Behind the Four Seasons' drag were three steps up to the entrance. The door was open; the lords could hear guitar music, amplified and tinny through the inadequate speakers. Tossin walked past the drag and inspected the interior of the coffeehouse. It was dark; light streamed only from a spotlight shining full upon the small stage. Slowly and steadily changing through the rotating, multicolored gel, the light shuddered on the features of the girl performer. Small candles were placed on the long tables, and ashtrays, and there was nothing else to see besides the customers. The humans sat crowded on long benches, listening to the empty songs, sadly, angrily, knowing they had been taken. A few lords sat at another table; they smiled and talked to each other as they would anywhere on Earth. They indulged themselves, moving easily among the humans; they carried themselves as if they did not really believe the humans existed.

Tossin turned away from the door. He stood on the stoop, and from the coffeehouse behind, dim colors played changes around him. He looked down at the drag, who was sorting out his ploys for the benefit of a young human couple.

"Are those songs authentic?" Tossin asked.

The drag stared over his shoulder, bewildered at being challenged by a lord. "Yeah. They write 'em themselves, don't they?"

"Tossin, come," said the mother. She disliked even the most businesslike dealings with humans, and the tour was causing deep agitation.

"And the drinks—do you know that they have no alcoholic content?" Tossin walked down the steps and rejoined his parents. He continued to speak to the drag, but he no longer looked at the human. "Why don't you tell these people that, also?"

"Tossin!" The mother took his hand in hers, pulling him away. Tossin felt for the first time the meaning of being a lord among humans: he was a lord, a *Lord!*

"You should not speak so with a human, Tossin," the mother said. "It lowers you to the human level."

Yes, Tossin thought, *yes* . . .

A crowd of humans stood outside the button shop, tourists, uptown people astounded by the grossness of the printed buttons in the window. They laughed, pointing out favorites so that wives and business partners would not miss them. Some of the buttons were old: rusty pins stuck through a creased blue cardboard backing; all were inane, sterile in concept, triggered to lose all humor after ten minutes' exposure. Periodically someone would find a button with a specially striking message. At these times the shop's door would open; the pressure of the crowd on the sidewalk would force several people into the store along with the original customer.

The lords stopped to examine the display window. The mother quickly grew disgusted with the trivial buttons; Tossin found himself amused in spite of himself. He went into the store, his parents following; the laughter of the humans quieted. When the lords entered, the humans turned from the window and continued down the street; the humans inside the store left quietly.

The shop was very small, a bathroom-sized intrusion into the brick building. It was lined along three sides with gray metal cabinets with sliding drawers. A different button was taped to the front of each drawer. Above the cabinets were mounted posters which were also for sale. The lords found little to hold their attention, feeling that the buttons and posters represented the self-indulgent portion of the human culture. They browsed; the single human employee watched resentfully.

Tossin stood with his left fingertips resting gently on his right breast. His right hand moved lightly from one button to another, touching them absently while he read them. Occasionally he glanced at the girl who managed the store; she returned his looks coldly, waiting for the lords to leave.

The girl was, in Tossin's opinion, very attractive by human standards. She was small, sitting on her stool and blinking like one of the lords' mythical elves. She had very long hair, much longer than the human fashion, and she wore it braided, draped over her left shoulder. Her eyes ticked off everything that happened in her store; she caught each detail, holding it against some mental checklist for identification. Tossin watched her watching; she was a new sort of human to him, the scarcest sort: she knew what she was doing. His interest bored and offended her. She turned her back to restock a glass case with cigarette papers.

A button caught Tossin's attention. Unlike the others, this one had no printed slogan. It was a simple button, divided in half vertically and colored light blue on the left half. The right half was further subdivided by horizontal lines into four sections, printed white, red, black, yellow. "What is this button?" he asked.

The girl scowled, her impatience and contempt in the click of tongue, in the movement of her eyes. "That's for the Unity freaks."

"What is the Unity?"

"Yeah, you don't know? Me and you and the niggers are all brothers. We got to get it together. Wear the button and everything'll be okay." She began to count the money in her black apron.

The mother looked annoyed; her arms were clasped tightly around her waist as she paced the front of the shop.

Tossin began to remove the Unity button taped to the front of the drawer. The human girl looked up and saw him. "The buttons are inside," she said.

Tossin glanced at her over his shoulder. She gave him a scornful look. "Don't do that! Open the drawer." Tossin took out four of the Unity buttons.

"I would like to purchase these," he said.

"Is that going to be all?"

"Yes."

"That'll be a dollar."

Tossin watched the ridicule flickering through her words. She expected the payment; in a way, she demanded it. Tossin's fresh feeling of superiority was shaken, but just a little. He was momentarily confused. He turned to his parents. "I like these, not because of the idea of Unity, but for the thin black dividing line." He took out a ten dollar bill. "How much tax is there?"

The human girl took the bill and put it in her apron. "I won't charge you tax." She gave Tossin eight singles in change. He held them stiffly for a moment, realizing that she had intentionally shortchanged him. She stared into his eyes; she was not mocking now, she was neither afraid nor insolent. He put the change away in his shoulder sling. The girl watched him carefully.

Tossin joined his parents. "Why do they sell themselves?" he asked. "Do they put prices on everything they have and everything they are? They speak of Unity, but why do they obstruct unity with a totally marketable, totally valueless culture?"

The spermfather nodded toward the human girl. "I don't know. But no one is forcing her to live like this. She has her own reasons."

The eggfather opened the door of the shop. The parents walked back out into the evening, leaving Tossin inside with the girl. For a short time they regarded each other. The last thing Tossin saw before he turned to leave was the human, sitting on a high stool, eating a slice of cold pizza. Her brows were drawn together: in concentration, in hatred, in restraint? Her eyes followed his, striking into his mind somehow. She was smiling, coldly, with so much bitterness. "Goodbye," she said. "Come again." At last he broke her hold and left.

After the next day he never thought of her again.

Amy Hutton is a poet by trade, when she is not busy at wifing and mothering. Like many stories, hers attempts to answer a question. In her own words: "Dreams, private thoughts, hopes, and fears: but when reality interferes, what is a dream?"

The Beholder's Eye

by Amy Hutton

His eyes followed the movements of her silvery body:
the turns, the swirling, the swaying on the night-colored
grass. He liked the warm look of her skin, the thick brown
hair that hid her face when she moved. She was a young
girl and he wouldn't touch her, only watch.

"Who is she?" asked the old one.

"Hell if I know," he said.

The old man sat slowly and cleaned his wire-framed
glasses. He braced his chin on his knee, watched her, and
spoke through his dark dry lips. "Do you think she'll do it?"

"No," the young one answered. He'd never seen her there
before. He knew nothing of her except that her naked body
entranced him.

"She's damn ugly. She must be a whore."

Her hair slid over her chest and caught in her mouth.
Her tender body seemed aware of some pulsating rhythm,
but she moved in silence.

The young man stood, keeping his eyes on the girl. He
was silent for a long while, scratching his left wrist nervously. Then he whispered, "How can you even begin to
appreciate her, old man?"

Making no noise that might interrupt her, he walked out
of the park, through the dimly lit alley, and into the steel
and concrete city.

The dishes in the back room clattered and the hot greasy
air made his face feel dirty. The fried eggs were cold and
slimy and they nauseated him. Joanne was waiting supper.

No, it was almost two-thirty. She'd be in bed waiting for him.

"Hey, mac, we're closin'."

"OK."

Joanne was limp, fat, and asleep. She breathed heavily, almost snoring. He felt that if he touched her, his hand would be engulfed in the folds of skin. Her mouth was wet and there was a spot of mayonnaise on her chin. Sitting on the edge of the bed, he forced himself to kiss the sweaty forehead and immediately felt the eggs coming up from his stomach. He let it all spill out on the rug, wiped his mouth on the sheet, and stepped over to the window.

Far off in the park light a silvery shadow stood very still and he knew doe-large eyes watched his window. Silently she radiated cleanliness; silk-white skin and water-pure eyes; God-clean hair and body.

He left the door open and ran, breathing the night air and feeling the wet concrete on his bare feet. Where the old man had sat stood a boy of twelve. His mud-caked jeans were torn and patched and he was hungry, bony thin.

"Hey, Ma," the boy yelled. "Come on home."

She slithered onto the grass and moved with it. Her brown hair entangled in her arms and covered her face. He could not touch her, ever. She was perfection, a god-child. And when the boy pulled her to her feet and guided her along the walk she glowed with a clean light. And when she sat by the young man's feet and lightly brushed his toes with her fingers, he was glad he'd come back.

"Do you think I am beautiful? Do you want me?" she whispered.

He nodded, knowing he could never hurt her, and she embraced his legs. "Thank you," she said.

She closed her eyes then, and as he watched, she grew old, wrinkled, and her hair became matted in dirty knots. The boy led her away, limping and dragging her feet reluctantly with her age. The young man laughed at himself and at her, at Joanne, at diner cooks and little boys.

Joanne's warm back arched and her fine hair smelled good to him. He could never leave her; he could never hurt her. She was his one hope for a new set of desires.

There have been many post-blowup stories, but few consider the real problems of reconstruction. Dave Skal, an eighteen-year-old college freshman, examines the problem with fresh vision. He writes: "I've always considered myself a rather pessimistic writer, but Robin insists this is not the case. The following story is my idea of a postwar society hampered not by radiation but by religion, ignorance, and fear. This is optimistic? Judge for yourself . . . " Yes, I echo. Judge for yourself.

Chains

by Dave Skal

The Reconstruction has reached a critical point. Precariously, like an infant, the country is beginning to stand on its own again. The Lake Erie Basin is one of the last strongholds to be broken, and Roberts knows it is going to be tough.

Decay. The omnipresent, never-settling dust of civil war. The gutted skyline of Cleveland over Lake Erie—a leftover, festering sink. It is much worse than he had expected, and the intense idealism that has sustained him weakens a little.

As he crests a small knoll near the shoreline, Roberts sees a slim young black woman sitting on the beach, scrawling things in the sand for a group of little children. They don't notice him. He looks out over the lake, and as the sludge laps against the shore, he sees a little girl, wading and splashing in the muck. He is vaguely nauseated and calls out to her—stupidly, he realizes. She turns, takes one look at him, and bursts into tears, waddling out of the water to the arms of the black woman, who regards him suspiciously.

He avoids her silent question of his identity, wipes wet red hair from his smooth brow, and says, "I'm looking for someone—a doctor who was through here. His name—"

"Stevens?" she asks, rising. Roberts can see now that her blackness is softened by something else—oriental, perhaps; that she has fiercely chiseled but delicate features.

"You . . . know him?"

"Not no more. He's dead."

"But how?"

"He's dead," she says, as if it really doesn't matter. She looks at the medical-equipment bag strapped across his shoulder. "Reconstruction?"

Something is wrong. The woman knows too much, displays an understanding that is not to be expected, at least not according to the information Roberts had received in the Detroit staging area.

"You know about Reconstruction?"

She doesn't answer, but gathers up her charges and prepares to leave.

Roberts follows, and she makes no objection.

They pass through sections where entire blocks have been razed, walking at least two miles to reach the settlement. The children don't seem to mind. Typically, the strongholders have holed up in crowded, fortresslike settlements. There is desolation—a sprawling ghetto of physical disease and psychological pestilence. Why use an atom bomb, thinks Roberts, when humans can wreak such destruction using the most primitive weapons? His depression increases.

He has, however, gleaned a few facts from the taciturn woman. Her name is Rose, and she is about twenty-five years old. She has been in the stronghold since the age of ten, when her parents, neutrals, were killed by highway marauders.

The hub of the settlement is the ruin of a bombed-out shopping center. As they arrive, women swarm about Rose, claiming their children, paying her with blackened canned goods or unrecognizable little cuts of meat. They are grateful, yet somehow . . . afraid. The last remnants of Middle America, Roberts thinks, victims of attack from both camps.

Rose turns to him, the dying sun bronzing her features. "Tragg will want to see you."

Tragg? Whatever his apprehensions, he is interested, and some of his depression lifts. *Take me to your leader,* he thinks, smiling. Rose does not smile back.

The Ward Healer Tragg is a big man, older than most strongholders, somewhere in his late thirties. Wispy hair crowns a Humpty-Dumpty head. Ruddy skin. He gesticulates constantly, forever putting on a show; he is, Roberts suspects, a compulsive performer.

"You realize, Roberts," he says resonantly, stroking Rose's hair, "that however altruistic your intentions, these people simply are not ready for medicine as *you* offer it.

I'm not saying they're totally impervious to progress, but just that they'll only accept modern technology on their own own terms and in ways they're familiar with."

That seems reasonable enough to Roberts. One of the first rules of missionary work he has been taught is never to force yourself on people. Suggest, direct—but always let them think they're working out their own problem.

Tragg continues: "Modern science will take hold here *eventually*—God knows it has to! But gradually. They don't want *medicine*—they want excitement, a show. Witch doctors. Magic." He seems to relish the sound of his own voice.

It is amazing, Roberts thinks, how much damage a single uneducated generation can do. A mere twenty years of darkness has resulted in almost medieval concretions of prejudice and fear.

Tragg gives him a room—a cell, really, for he has taken up residence in the fortresslike jail building. Roberts sleeps fitfully, dreaming of a flower, a black rose. . . .

The Meeting is held in the stripped interior of an old movie theater. Mildew blooms across the yellow screen in a living Rorschach; a huge red cross has been painted in its center. There is a narrow apron from which the service can be conducted.

And there is Tragg.

He prays. He leads them in song. He calls down the wrath of God and he harangues them like a demagogue. It is a church service, it is a revival, it is bible-belt fundamentalism alive again, and it is more. Women scream, cry, tear at their clothing, and writhe on the floor. Men chant, stomp their feet, their torches sending up monster shadows of Tragg to play on the screen. He becomes unintelligible, spouting forth gibberish at a sea of hungry, pleading, penitent faces. The afflicted. The diseased.

And Tragg heals them!

It happens, yet it doesn't. It is emotionally devastating to Roberts.

And Roberts is the leader's stooge, treating real illnesses, Tragg consecrating his tools, proving *himself* the healer. The strongholders, true believers all, don't seem to connect the needles and medications directly with their recoveries. *Tragg* is their god—it is *his* magic that cures them—anything else would be heresy.

The girl, Rose, continues to intrigue Roberts that evening after the meeting. His question to her—and Tragg—

concerning his predecessor are met with polite circumventions. And there is her enigmatic relationship with Tragg. At first it strikes Roberts that she is the leader's mistress. But no: their relationship is something far stranger. The way Tragg talks to her, touches her . . . it is, Roberts realizes, the relationship between a human being and a cat. In Britain, he recalls, black cats were once said to bring good luck. Here . . .

"Mr. Rob!" A woman's voice; fearful, desperate.

He awakes with a start. One of the women from the settlement is kneeling over his bunk.

"What is it?"

"Oh, please, Mr. Rob," she says. "I can't find Tragg. I know I'm supposed to wait till Meeting—but my little girl, Ann. She's so sick—"

Roberts doesn't know what to do. The woman must have seen him at one of the meetings. She is alone and obviously expects him to accompany her. If the child is really ill, and Tragg isn't to be found—

"All right. Where is she?"

The woman leads him to a house on the outskirts of the settlement. There are about ten families living in the crumbling split-level—more if you count this woman and her child holed up in an abandoned automobile in the weed-infested back yard.

"Here she is, my Ann—in the back."

In the back seat of the rusted-out Ford is a little girl. She is perspiring heavily, her frail body wracked with chills. It doesn't take Roberts long to diagnose typhoid. He checks his kit for a serum.

The families have come out of the house, apparently, ready for a breast-beating frenzy, a ritual medicine show. He ignores them and prepares a syringe.

"Mr. Rob—the singing. Aren't you . . . ?"

"No—there'll be no singing tonight." The child needs rest and quiet. Damn Tragg! His insane "services" are doing more harm than good. Roberts is irritable and busy, and yet a small part of his mind calls him fool for forbidding the singing.

The strongholders are stupefied, but they watch intently as Roberts gives the child an injection. She whimpers. He orders her taken to the house. The strongholders are incredulous but still in fear of him because of his connection with Tragg, and they do as they are told. Roberts gives simple instructions for the girl's care, hoping they will understand, and promises to return the next day.

Tragg is furious. He screams. He rants. He threatens to kill. Rose tries to placate him, and he slaps her in the face. "If I didn't need you, Roberts—!" He becomes incoherent.

"You weren't here, Tragg! Was I supposed to let the little girl *die?*"

"Yes!" he screams. "Better than letting those cretins know what's—" He catches himself. "Don't you realize how damaging this could be? All my work—"

"Really, Tragg! You can't keep them ignorant forever!"

"I can do whatever I want! I'm in charge here! Who do you think *you* are?"

Roberts storms out. Tragg doesn't seem to notice, so intent is he on venting his anger.

As Roberts expects, the little girl improves. By the second day he feels sure she will recover.

On the third day she is dead.

He is sickened when the mother comes staggering by the jail carrying the corpse of her child. The woman's eyes are blank and uncomprehending; she moans softly.

Roberts comes out to her. He stretches out his hands as if to relieve her of her terrible burden, but she has become defensive, hugging the body closer, running her fingers through the straggly hair. A sizable crowd has gathered. Roberts sweats profusely.

Then something happens. The woman's eyes lose their glaze, blink. She is suddenly aware of what she is holding. She screams.

The crowd backs off, scatters, as the woman breaks down. Roberts is left alone in the middle of the street with her, this tragic woman and her cold, dead child. He tries to talk to her, to find out what has happened, but he is helpless before her wall of tears.

He leaves her and goes back to his cell. He stands at the window and stares for a long while. What has happened? It can't have been the typhoid. Unless . . .

A stunning blow at the base of his skull prevents any further speculation.

Painfully, he regains consciousnes in his cell. It is somehow different. Chains. The cell had been sealed, lashed shut, padlocked.

His head pounds. Tragg. He checks the chains. Heavy, secure, and he doesn't have much strength. Tragg. Dammit, where is Tragg? After all, Tragg needs him.

Or does he?

He sits down, weak and dizzy. Perhaps he has become a threat—

A sound. Low, susurrating, distant. Singing. He drags himself to the barred window and strains to see. Nothing. But the noise is louder now—it sounds as if a Meeting is being held right out in the streets.

He yells for Tragg, Rose, anyone.

The chanting rises up to fill the night, to echo dismally throughout the deserted jail. There is a primitive quality to the sound that knots his stomach in fear. The march of Haitian *zombis*. Trumpets on Judgment Day—

"Rob." It is Rose, and she has a key.

He should feel relief, but anger comes instead.

"The little girl—Tragg killed her, didn't he? Or was it you?"

"No. Tragg did it." She fumbles with the padlock, the chains begin to fall away. She explains: "He tried to make me, but I wouldn't. They found out—everything—and went after him. Please, Rob, hurry—we can't let them—"

"Just a minute," he says, holding her by the shoulders, shaking her. "And Stevens? What about him?"

"He died—"

"Murder?"

"No—an accident. But Tragg was using him too. He was afraid he was losing control—"

He releases her, and they go out into the streets. Darkness. Wind. Desolation. They head instinctively for the theater.

It appears to be empty. One of the rusted doors has been ripped from its hinges. Rose's breathing is heavy, panicked.

The auditorium is dark, and they pick their way slowly down the aisle. The stench of mildew. Roberts' heart is pumping wildly.

There is something on the stage.

He doesn't have to ask; a crumpled cardboard pack is thrust into his hand. He tears out a match, strikes it.

The tiny flame flares up, for a moment illuminating the cavernous room. Rose screams.

It is Tragg. Eyes rolled upward, as if in supplication, he has been nailed to the center of the Rorschach, nailed to the painted cross. He is quite dead.

Later: Outside it is chill. A slight fog, the promise of rain. Rose comes out, dazed. She has been inside for two hours, keening, mourning her master. Now she stands next to Roberts, stares straight ahead, waiting.

A crowd begins to collect. Pleading faces, lost, begging, expecting. Rose's fingertips touch his arm, tentatively.

Uncertainly, he takes her hand, and the rain begins. He wonders if he can find a bible, or remember the service for the burial of the dead.

Fantasy:
Many Mansions and Hovels

by Fritz Leiber

The word "fantasy" gripes me.

It has too many meanings.

Also, it is much too frequently used to downgrade or write off ideas and stories as frivolous, trivial, grotesque, dreamy, psychedelic, crackpot, impossible, childish, romantic, feminine, foolish, ridiculous.

(Actually, the words "fantasy" and "fiction" mean exactly the same thing. All fiction, even the most realistic. Farrell's *Studs Lonigan* is a fantasy: it never really happened just that way anywhere on earth—even Chicago!—or elsewhere.)

Fiction or literature (*you* decide how to rate the stuff), "fantasy" has been used to describe:

—The plotty gamboling of fairies back in the days when they were slim, girlish figures four inches high, winged like dragonflies (recall Disney's *Fantasia*), who danced on unfallen autumn leaves at the bottom of the garden, rather than loitered in men's public lavatories and accosted sensitive looking weak-chinned strangers. If the fuzz was involved, it was always a comic Irish cop with a hard blue hat two feet high, who could be squared with a jug of Irish whiskey (he called fairies leprechauns);

—Beautiful, platonic romances between grave, impish little girls and charming middle-aged men, who were generally professors with a profound knowledge of mathematics or metaphysics. *Lolita* put an end to that;

—*All* science fiction, even the "hard" sort, which strives to speculate and peer into the future without any absolutely

129

unnecessary contradictions of the theories of modern science and the facts of modern technology; it takes the wide view; at its best it is truer to the large world of today than, say, the narrow-focus, decadent-backwater fiction found in many of the stories of William Faulkner, John Steinbeck, Truman Capote, etc.;

—Science fiction which mixes in large elements of romance and adventure and isn't always as careful about its facts. This sort is sometimes called science fantasy or even pseudoscience, and at its worst, "space opera";

—Shamelessly wish-fulfilling yarns of supermen of vast muscular skills and powers—and even mental and extrasensory ones. There is never a question as to whether the sneering, snarling, seemingly all-powerful villain will be defeated at the end. Edgar Rice Burroughs is the widest-read of these with his tales of Tarzan and of John Carter of Virginia and Mars;

—Hip psychedelic visions, which often churn too much, set down, sometimes in the fashion of someone under—or *as if* under—the influence of LSD, etc. His product is generally "heavy," to use the current argot, and he himself interestingly knowledgeable about drugs. Here by amusing coincidence a leading figure is William S. Burroughs, author of *The Naked Lunch, Nova Express,* etc.;

—The so-called Gothic novel, involving a beautiful, menaced heroine, an often stupid hero, a Byronic villain with mysterious powers and purposes, a *soupçon* of supernatural horror, and an antique mansion or castle designed chiefly to have an eerie moon rise over it. Quite recently you couldn't have bribed a publisher to put "Gothic" on the cover of a book. Now the word is intensely popular again. But the Gothic novel has always tended toward soap opera;

—The straight supernatural horror story, which chiefly aims to arouse in the reader (almost as pornography aims to arouse sexual excitement) a fear stranger and more metaphysical than that induced by the illusion of uncaged lions and homicidal maniacs prowling *almost* silently outside the window at dusk. Such tales may be backgrounded by a Christian cosmos or (rarely) that of another religion—or a mythos of the author's own devising. H. P. Lovecraft, Montague Rhodes James, Arthur Machen, and Charles Williams are examples. I like this sort of story and write quite a few of them myself, but I like to link them to present-day issues and happenings rather than set them, say, in the pastiche world of Victorian cloaks and top hats. Lovecraft operated on the same principles;

—So-called sword (or swordplay) and sorcery, or heroic fantasy stories, adventures set in medieval-barbaric worlds invented by the author, worlds where magic and cold steel work about equally well. I like them, provided they have the bite of current reality without becoming satires, allegories, or mere thud-and-blunder. They range from the crude superman novels noted above (of course, there are also serious superman novels concerned with the evolution of future man and other beings intelligent beyond our present scope) to Robert E. Howard's irregular Conan stories (sometimes great, sometimes ghastly) to Tolkien's *The Lord of the Rings,* a vastly popular trilogy I can't reread; I think the reason so many young people went for it so strongly was that it was almost the first fantasy they encountered; they grew up in an era when sociology-minded schoolmasters thought fantasy was bad for the young and instead loaded them down with cliché-stories of the "happy" childhoods of Sioux Indians, Eskimos, and little bright-skirted Bulgarians; also, the Ring novels whooped it up in a cynical age for the worthy ideals of nobility, rescue-the-oppressed, and the brotherhood of good adventurers;

—Allegory: ninety-nine times out of hundred the dullest fantasy going. Following an exact one-to-one parallelism between the characters and events in an imaginary world and those in the world today is generally an exercise for morons; a little of this sort of thing can be stimulating, though;

—Stories heavy on myth and legendry: *see* sword and sorcery, for the most part;

—Stories heavy on symbolism. This at its worst is better than allegory, since the reader can shift around between several or many levels of interpretation, as an analyst does with a dream. Any story of even ankle depth involves symbolism and its plot is invariably some well-established myth or legend;

—Stories (here we get a trifle technical or in-group) involving conditions or events which modern science deems not only highly improbable but absolutely impossible: incarnate gods, witchcraft, werewolves, intelligent creatures living in a raindrop, telekinesis, cats who conduct highly intelligent conversations, and so forth (while science fiction concerns itself always with the possible, even if highly improbable). But even here we at once get into contradictions. Time travel, long the darling device of even hard science fiction (start with *The Time Machine* by H. G. Wells and and let the titles roll), is today surely considered an absolute impossibility by practically all scientists and even way back by St. Thomas Aquinas. And so it is—maybe. (There speaks the fantasy writer! And the science-fiction writer, too.)

Well, I have spun out the subcategories (ugh!) of fantasy long enough—thirteen of them, unlucky number— and maybe too long even at that. But they literally could go on forever. Categories (ugh again!) and genres (another word I love to hate!) are valid and useful only insofar as they make it easier to discuss stories. They are no more than pigeonholes in a vast desk and have no more to say about the importance and truth of papers that are shoved into them—and often refiled.

A half century or so ago Rudyard Kipling could publish in a book of mostly mainstream (ugh a final time!) short stories a hard science-fiction piece ("With the Night Mail"), a bit of science fantasy ("Wireless"), a yarn of reincarnation ("The Greatest Story Ever Told"), and tales of supernatural horror ("The Mark of the Beast" and "The Phantom 'Rickshaw") without editors getting on their ears or critics becoming hoarse from shouting that someone had been writing beneath himself. Were Dostoevsky and Wassermann rebuked for turning out detective stories when they wrote *The Brothers Karamozov* and *The Maurizius Case?*

Why this ridiculous fuss over genres and subgenres?— when every new story is, however slightly, a new creation, unique. Sometimes I think that today every critic, editor, writer even, even every reader has developed a crazy compulsion to become a specialist or subspecialist, exactly as the scientists and doctors have done, in some little realm he rules alone, or at least can count himself a prince of.

But the writers of fiction are not scientists or doctors. We expect from them entertainment, empathy, insight, illumination, not the literal truth.

What is really at stake? Human imagination! Which before all else demands freedom, including the very important freedom to break down all partitions between thoughts and experiences, to avoid specialization always.

To me it boils down to this: any fantasy, fiction, or story is anchored to or has fixed reference points along two shores, which may be called today outer and inner space (rather than the stuffy-sounding "objective" and "subjective"). Science itself is anchored solely to outer space: it consists of observations and experiments which anyone can repeat with the requisite effort and get identical results. The sort of autobiographical novel which hardly does more than change names is anchored close to the shore of outer space, though it has ties oversea.

Fantasy, while maintaining looser, yet still unbreakable ties with both shores, always rides closer to the middle of the ocean, where things are more exciting. One may think of it as additionally linked to great islands called Story and Myth.

I believe that the stories in this book are of that sort.

Robert Thurston demonstrates his versatility with this story. He also demonstrates that time can be manipulated by something (in Lewis Mumford's words) "more wonderful than H. G. Wells' technological contraption."

By way of a preface, Thurston adds: "Is there really life after birth? Probably there is."

Anaconda

by Robert Thurston

—Running through the strung-net jungle, cut off from familiar terrain and knowing it's better to be cut off from familiar carnage, looking up and seeing strange curvatures in palm fronds, looking down at your army-issue undershorts. Only a fuckup like you would be racing through enemy jungle in only your undershorts—

Willie had a hook nose. It came straight down to here, like it was headed for Grecian beauty, and then, when it was well on its way, took a straight plunge down to the tip. A thin mouth: in some lights, with shadows darkening its corners, looking like a baton, like it could be twirled on your baby finger and neon would flash on and off for a finale. His eyes used their sockets for a hiding place.

—Don't panic just because you don't know which of these many noises could be caused by a Jap foot gently dislodging a mossy stone that's been stuck up in a fork between branches for maybe fifty years—

He had a long forward-pointing chin, which sometimes he could thrust out bravely and pretend that the rest of his face had somehow reassembled and showed some courage, too.

—Maybe some young Filipino boy (later to be a sellout houseboy to some belly-bulging planter, a fat flag-waver shouting Yessir, Admiral Dewey, there's millions to be had here in these lush antediluvian islands hardly touched by civilized man)

—this young Filipino boy (later to tell the planter where to shove his mangoes, and then to return to his ripe lovely

135

Filipino chick and ball her in the civilized ways he'd learned
from the planter's wife)

—this young Filipino boy (later to endure his teeth
rotting and the chick's skin fading from Gauguin colors to
sadder and drabber hues)

—this young Filipino boy (later to get thin and feel his
bones become brittle and one day experience a panoramic
cough that disconnects something inside; dying all curled
up and looking dehydrated)

—this young Filipino boy walking in the jungle flung a
few stones in the air. One of them sailed upward and it
lodged in the fork (between the thighs, sailed right in there
between the old mossy thighs). Or maybe it hit up higher
first and bounced a couple of times, and *then* wound up in
that branch gathering moss and insect droppings for fifty-
sixty years until the booted careless slip of a sniper who
hears you, Willie, and is waiting to zero in on you. He's an
expert, a Kamikaze rifleman: one bullet which zings right
in on target, goes clean through, takes a smooth sweeping
arc, and comes back to finish off the rifleman himself. So he
has to make the shot count. Don't be scared. Just a
Kamikaze rifleman and his boomerang bullet—

Lines in an interconnecting network all over his flaking
skin. His hair reduced to a few thick strands which became
white toward the end.

His body was gradually eaten away from the inside by
unsocial drinking. Finally it collapsed inward, pulled his
shoulders forward, bent his back. Even his good suit looked
like a random choice from a Goodwill rack.

—Keep on running. It's a big island and you might
stumble onto our side again and go to another island and
climb John Wayne Hill and watch Tony Curtis and some
other guys put up the flag, long may it wave. If you'd
lived, Willie, you could slap a flag decal on the back window
of your car. But that's too far into the future, way beyond
your future, Willie—

At the funeral home the main theme was regret. Dressed-
up eulogies for a wasted life. Purgation: the family decline
set in satin.

Nobody remarked on her absence. The widow. Or is an
ex-wife an ex-widow? *The ex-widow came to the coffin and
tried to remember who had died. And when.*

Collapse, fall, feel a hundred insects leap onto your body.
Let the Jap bastard draw a bead on you. If he's there. Wipe
your sweating palms on your standard-issue undershorts—

Everybody talked about him lying in his blood at the

bottom of the splintered stairs. An air of mystery. Suspicion of murder. Purgation: unnatural death so much better than natural. *The ex-widow demanded an investigation. The inspector said, Sure, anything for you, baby. As an affirmation of conviction, he grabbed her net-hosed leg on the upswing.*

—Listen for stonefall, for the crack of an arm stretching, the caressing of a rifle barrel. He's not really up there. He is really up there—

The grocery clerk and the handyman had all the good stories. They let them out sporadically, like notions-department gifts (mechanical, useful). *The ex-widow confessed to the crime. Everyone knew she lied, but she had to be arrested and taken away. To satisfy the reporters. She grabbed a coffin handle and pulled the coffin off its moorings. She dragged it with her out of the funeral home. The policemen had difficulty fitting it into the patrol wagon.*

The metal-clangers came and stood over the coffin and cried. Their timing was good, since the grocery clerk and the handyman were running out of funny stories. They stood at the coffin and cried, and made the others carefully examine the lush antediluvian ornaments of the shadowy, palm-fronded funeral home. "He could hack it," a metal-clanger muttered on his way out. *At the hearing the ex-widow produced dramatic evidence that she was being fucked at the estimated time of death. Some time was wasted determining the estimated time of fuck. Under the prosecutor's intense questioning, the ex-widow meticulously avoided the use of the word. She said she'd had an intruder in the storehouse, as if the storehouse had not known many intruders since the lock was dissolved. When the judge dismissed the case, reporters dived to the ground to take her picture.*

The funeral itself was a long drive and a short drop. At the graveside someone wondered if there had been a time, just before he stopped the world, when he was ready to put his thumb against central Asia and distribute his fingers along the Americas with maybe a crooked baby finger resting on the Australian coastline and give the whole sphere a few more spins. (Let a fingernail scrape against the Philippines while the globe turns.) A time when it might have been worth it to have the two-timing bitch back. To take her in again and let her come toward his bed in that nightgown, that nightgown that looked as if it might melt off that exquisite body at that moment. *The ex-widow curled her toes over the side of the grave and stood quite still, the only movement coming from her dress turning to wax.*

—Could you have swallowed the family pride and taken her back in spite of all the cracking old rooms where she'd lain on gray pillows and watched ceiling spiderwebs shuddering at drafts of chill air? As you squirm in the musty undergrowth, daintily moving sideways from erratically moving thing on the underside of a leaf, and hear in the night a dislodged stone, and look with scared eyes at the canopy of jungle, and rub your sweaty palms on your standard-issue undershorts, and think of what it will be like when you get home(and now your fingers tremble, wanting to get a good grab at her lush antediluvian snatch), could you have forgiven her then if she'd spread away the undergrowth and had looked down on you, your hands in stopped motion against your undershorts, and slowly, slowly had wet her lips with her tongue?

I can add nothing to Estelle Butler's introduction to this story: "Writers must be among the very few people who can use to their creative advantage the negative emotions of personal depression. 'Crossover,' the product of such depression, is a work born of despair and loneliness. It investigates the lengths to which one might go to find relief."

Crossover

by Octavia Estelle Butler

At work that day they put her to soldering J9 connectors into a harness and they expected her to do twice as many as everyone else. She did, of course, but her only reward was resentment from the slower girls down the line because she was making them look bad. At lunch a couple of them came to her solitary corner table and told her to ease off. That was how it was. If she did good work, other employees resented her and her lead man ignored her. If her work fell off, other employees ignored her and her lead man wrote "bad attitude" on her work review. She hadn't had a raise in two years. She would have quit long ago had she not been afraid to try to start all over again at a new place where the people might be even worse.

Through the afternoon all she wanted was two or three aspirins and sleep. She had not had a headache for three months and this one scared her.

As usual, though, she managed to finish the day. When she got off she even felt hungry enough to make a side trip to the store for a can of something for dinner. It was her headache that drove her to make the shorter trip to the liquor store instead of going to the grocery store. *It was her headache.*

The liquor store was on a corner only two blocks from where she worked. It was across from a pool hall and a bar and near a cheap hotel. That made it a gathering place for certain kinds of people.

There was a crowd on the corner when she got there. Besides the usual drunks and prostitutes there was a group of teen-age boys who were bored enough not to ignore her. For

140

a moment they whispered to each other, laughing. Then as she passed them the calls began.

"Hey, Jeffery, there go your old woman!"

"Lady, you sure shouldn't have let that car run over your face!"

"Hey, lady, this boy say he go for you!"

A wino sidled up to her. "Come on, baby, let's you and me go up to my room."

She jerked herself out of the alcoholic cloud that surrounded him and went into the store. The clerk there was rude to her because he was rude to everyone. He did not matter any more than the others. The wino tried to catch her by the arm as she left.

"Come on, you not in too big a hurry to talk to me . . ."

She almost ran from him, barely controlling her disgust. She left him standing swaying slightly in the middle of the street staring after her.

As she neared the hotel she noticed someone standing in the narrow doorway. A man who had something wrong with his face. *Something* . . . She almost turned and went back toward the drunk. But the man stepped out and came over to her during her moment of hesitation. She looked around quickly, her eyes wide with fear. No one was paying any particular attention to her. Even the wino had begun to move away.

The man said, "I don't go away if you ignore me." He had a scar that ran the length of his face from eye to chin on the left side. When he talked or smiled or frowned, it moved and she could watch it and ignore everything else. Sometimes she could even avoid listening to him. Now she watched it and thought quickly.

"So you got out." There was nothing but bitterness in her voice.

He laughed and the scar curved, wormlike. "This morning. I expected you to be there to meet me."

"No you didn't. I told you three months ago you could stay locked up forever as far as I was concerned."

"And you didn't mean it then either. Ninety days. That's a long time."

"You should have thought about that before you got into the fight."

"Yeah. Man hits me and pulls a knife. I had all the time in the world to remember you didn't want me fighting." He paused. "You know, you could have come to see me just once while I was in."

"I'm sorry." Toneless. False without any attempt to hide the falseness.

He made a sound of disgust. "The day you're sorry for anything . . ."

"All right, I'm not sorry. I don't give a damn." She narrowed her eyes and threw the words at him. "Why don't you go find a girl who will come to see you next time you get put away?"

The scar hardly moved when he spoke. "Things changed that much in three months?"

"They changed that much."

"You find somebody else to kind of help you forget about me?"

Now she laughed, once, with absolute bitterness. "Not one, baby, dozens! Didn't you see them all back there on the co⁻ er? They couldn't wait to get to me!"

⌐uietly: "All right. All right, be quiet." He put an arm .ound her and walked with her toward her apartment.

Later, when they had eaten and made love, she sat head in hands trying not to think while he talked at her. She paid no attention until he asked a question that she wanted to answer.

"Don't you ever wish for a decent-looking guy to come and get you out of that factory and out of this dump you live in . . . and away from me?"

"What would a decent-looking guy want with me?"

Instead of answering he said, "You still have that bottle of sleeping pills in your medicine cabinet?"

When she did not answer, he went to look. "Nonprescription now," he said when he came back. "What happened to the others?"

"I poured them down the toilet."

"Why?"

Again she did not answer.

After a moment, he said more gently, "When?"

"When I . . . when they put you in jail."

"And you acted like you didn't expect to see me again."

She shook her head. "I didn't."

"I don't want to die any more than you do."

She jumped and glanced at him. He knew better than to talk like that. He did it to hurt her. That was all.

She said, "I'd rather be dead than here picking up where we left off three months ago."

"Then why'd you throw out the pills?"

"So I would live. Without you."

He smiled. "And when did you decide you couldn't?"

She threw the heavy glass ashtray beside the bed. It flew wide of him, dented the wall behind him, and broke into three pieces.

He looked from the pieces to her. "You would have made your point better if you had tried to hit me."

She began to cry and she was not aware when the crying became screaming. "Get out of here! Leave me alone! *Leave me alone!*"

He didn't move.

Then her neighbor was pounding on the door to find out what all the noise was about. She calmed herself enough to open it, but while she was reassuring the woman that everything was all right, he came up behind her and stood there. She did not have to look around to know he was there. Still she did not come near losing control until her neighbor said, "You must be lonesome over here by yourself. Why don't you come around to my apartment and talk for a while?"

It was as though her neighbor were playing a stupid childish joke on her. It should have been a joke. Somehow, she got rid of the woman without breaking down.

Then she turned and stared at the man—at the scar marring a face that had never been handsome. She shook her head, crying again but paying no attention to her tears. He seemed to know better than to touch her.

After a while she got her coat and started out the door.

"I'm going with you."

The look she gave him contained all the stored-up viciousness of the day. "Do whatever you want." She saw fear in his eyes for the first time.

"Where are you going?"

She said, "You didn't have to meet me on the street today. Or come to the door just now. You didn't have to talk about . . ."

"Jane, where are you going?"

There were few things she hated more than her own name. In all the time they had been together, he could not have used it more than twice. She slammed the door in his face.

"What am I that I could need you anyway?" She wished she had said the words to him but it didn't matter. It was just another of the things she didn't have the courage to do. Like accepting the loneliness or dying or . . .

She retraced her steps back to the liquor store. The boys had gone but the wino was still there leaning against a

telephone pole and holding a bag shaped by the bottle inside it.

"So you come back, huh?" He couldn't stand at a distance and talk. He had to put his face right up next to hers.
It was an act of will for her not to vomit.

He thrust the bag at her. "You can have a little bit if you
want. I got some more in my room. . ."

She stared at the bottle for a moment, then almost
snatched it from him. She drank without giving herself
time to taste or think or gag. She had lived around drunks
most of her life. She knew that if she could get enough
down, nothing would matter.

She let the wino guide her toward the hotel. There was
a scarfaced man coming toward them from down the block.
She sucked another swallow from the bottle and waited for
him to vanish.

Another post-blowup story, or is it? Has the blowup already taken place? Lynnda Stevenson's story can be read as a picture of current reality, the post-Berkeley society. Or is it a picture of a future in which T. S. Eliot's whimper is the universal condition?

Miss Stevenson prefaces her story with this passage from Jerzy Kosinski's *The Painted Bird:*

"They collided with or charmed one another, hugged or trampled one another, but everyone thought only of himself. . . . Like the moutain peaks around us, we looked at one another, separated by valleys, too high to pass unnoticed, too low to touch the heavens."

Norman:
Friends and Other Strangers

by Lynnda Stevenson

Five-thirty on a Monday morning. I'm still half asleep, and I wish to sleep longer, but I can taste and smell the dawn, and I know I must soon get up. I turn to see if he is still beside me. He is. Sleeping soundly. The dawn plays on his features and casts a gray glow on his bronzed face. He will soon be awake and we will pack the gear and move on.

He has chosen a spot where violets and clover grow. I know he cannot tolerate enclosures of any kind. He must be free. He is. Freedom, he says, is a dream and love is understanding. Sometimes I do not understand what he says, but the words are poetry, and I listen and pretend.

When I met him we were children, and more afraid of ourselves than we were of each other. I look back on those years with a certain sadness, although they are the happiest times of my life. I suppose I look back with sadness because things have changed and I have not. But the memories are kind and soft and I am thankful for the warmth of them on cold and lonely mornings.

Six o'clock. He'll want to screw as soon as he wakes up. Sometimes he says make love; sometimes screw; and sometimes fuck. But there is no love as far as he's concerned. He told me once that he dreamed he said I love you to me. But that was all he said. His dreams are his life. He doesn't know the meaning of the word reality. He spends his afternoons scheming, his nights dreaming, and his mornings making love. He only has time for me in the morning. The rest of the day he is alone. I'm alone all the time.

Seven-thirty. Soon we will be gone from here. He will

146

expect me to be wide-awake and as eager to move on as he is. He should know me well enough to realize that I do not always wish to travel. That I would like to be in one spot just long enough to have a memory of it. Or to meet one person; but all the memories I have are of him, and of being alone. Alone in meadows where wild flowers grow waist-high and there have been no people ever. That's what he promised me. He promised to take me to places where there were wild flowers and no people; to live alone and feast on rainbow trout stuffed with wild raspberries and to drink strong tea when nights are cold. To write alone and tell the beauty of loneliness; to be free and owe no one a thing. It's another dream, another lie, another brick in the nonexistent castle we live in. He can't leave his dreams; and he won't include me in them.

I wasn't with him when he took his last look at reality. I did not hear the dog bark just before the mortar attack began. I did not see the lights or feel the pain. If I had been there then, I'd be in his dream now. For that moment has obsessed him. His poetry tells it and his eyes still see it. All the dreams and plans we had before he left are gone.

He used to be a poet; and part of him still is. But now he's a hard-ass and he likes to hurt others because once he was hurt. I used to think that I was the one who hurt him—and it hurt me to think it; but I know now that he hurt himself, and I know it because he changed and I did not.

Silence. He is planning a scheme. We need money. That means we'll have to cut down more pennies. When you cut the rim off a penny—the coin is the size of a dime. He'll cut them down until he has enough for food—or until he gets tired—or until his ankle begins to hurt. Then I'll cut five so I can buy a pack of cigarettes. He refuses to support my habit. I just smoked a cigarette. He regards this as a weakness. He reminds me once more of the money we could save if I did not smoke; and I silently hate him because he is breaking a rule of the game. He is finding fault with me; he expects me to change to please him. He has changed, but I haven't and he finds fault with my changelessness.

Nine o'clock. We are sitting in the grass a hundred yards from a dirt road. There is an apple tree nearby, so I have picked up some of the best and put them in the pack. He has finally settled himself comfortably. His ankle hurts and he is complaining. He tells me I don't know how much it hurts. I can't comprehend the agony.

I have no compassion. I am a worthless bitch. Shut the hell up. I grab the tin-snips and a handful of pennies. I'll show him. He moans about his ankle. He won't appreciate anything I do. He never does. I'll have to sit in the shade. The sun makes my hands sweat and it's hard enough to cut down pennies. My hands. My God, they're ugly. They've aged so much—my face probably has too—but it's been so long since I looked in a mirror, I almost forget what I look like. But I can see my hands and they're old and ugly. The nails are broken and dirty. There are calluses on my left hand from cutting pennies. My left hand. It looks so funny without the ring.

There's still a white circle where it used to be. The skin will tan eventually and no one will ever know that I once wore a wedding band. We hocked it three days ago in Phoenix. It didn't matter anyway. We aren't married, so it didn't mean anything. That's what he said. It meant something to me though. But I couldn't tell him about it.

I wish I could cry. But I cannot remember what it is like and it frightens me because it must mean that I am dead. Dead. Maybe that wouldn't be so bad. What am I doing now? Not living. Freedom is a dream and love is understanding. Good. I do not know the meaning of either. How can he have changed so much?

I used to blame the war and the establishment for his failure; but it's all his fault. He is a big talker and that's all. I have heard about his plans for years and I have never seen one made real. He loves to dream. He's dreaming right now. Soon he'll tell me the great idea he's had. But he'll wait until I have a few more coins cut down. I know; maybe he'll decide to publish a book of poetry. If I had a penny for every book of poetry he was going to publish, I wouldn't be cutting these damned things down right now. He'll never publish anything because he'll never write anything. He used to. But that was before he changed. I don't write much any more, either—but I don't sit around under apple trees and pretend I'm going to.

He has just told me his plan. Yes. I was right. He will publish a book called *Friends and Other Strangers* and will dedicate it to me. That's kind. It will include poetic essays and poems describing our friends. He asks me if I think it is a good title. Yes. Dylan thought so, too. He explains that he knows it is a line from Dylan's "Gates of Eden." That is why he is dedicating the book to me. Because of my fondness for Dylan. I knew he'd have some reason for it. He just wouldn't dedicate a book to me because I've lived with him for three years, ever since they trashed Washington. I wonder if he knows, deep down inside, as surely as I do that not one page will ever be finished. It's a nice thought, though. At least he'll forget about his ankle for a while. He'll be planning the book. And it will give me a chance to remember the old days. Before he left and came back a changed person.

Twelve-thirty. We have finally found a place that still has a few vending machines. We have twenty-five pennies. I'll go without cigarettes. That means we'll have a half-decent lunch. We'll get milk. Fifteen cents. Use two pennies. Get a nickel in change. We'll do all right today. Phoenix is a good town for vending machines. He likes it here. I don't. I like cold and wet and dreary days. The sun likes Phoenix too much. I wish it would shine on the other side of the street for a while. My skin has never been this brown. Our friends would probably not recognize me. Our friends. That is what we talked about the whole way into town. The old gang.

He is going to immortalize them in prose and poetry. They are already immortal to me. He is bringing back memories I didn't know I had. We have even laughed a few times since we left the apple tree. His favorite memories are not mine—but at least we are sharing something. He likes to talk about the sign they put on the cigarette machine in the Student Union at our college. ("If any more pennies are found in the machine, the machine will be removed.") But we didn't stop getting fifty cents' worth of cigarettes for five pennies; and they didn't remove the machine. It's funny, but he didn't mind cutting down pennies then. There were four of us. I wonder what Meredith and Richard are doing. We were so close then, but I haven't thought of them in months.

We all had nicknames, he reminds me. How could I forget? Those names fit us so perfectly. Meredith was the Maid. Richard was the Mist. He was always so unhappy. Maybe he's happy now. I think he and the Maid were in love. I never asked; I assumed they were, so they must have been. I remember saying how perfect it was that they were in love because we could say that Meredith was the Maid of the Mist.

He wants to know if I remember what his nickname was. Of course. He was the Mormon. Norman the Mormon. I don't know if he is a devout Mormon or not. I don't know much about religion. But he likes this part of the country, and he likes caves, so maybe he is a Mormon. My nickname. He is laughing now. The Myth. It was such a perfect nickname. I was very proud of it. I did not want people to know me. I was happiest when I was most mysterious. I always told half-truths; and no one could ever tell when I was lying. I never let anyone see the real me—well, almost never. It was so much more fun to play the game. Keep them guessing. The game was fun—but I lost. I became the Myth. I did not know myself any better than anyone else knew me. He says it will all be in the book. Too bad it will never be written. By tonight he will have forgotten all about it. But it is good to talk like this. And to laugh. He does not complain about his ankle. And I do not feel so alone.

Three-thirty. If I could cry, I would. In fact, I think I did cry when I stood at that window. We passed the pawn shop where we sold my ring. I saw it in the window and stopped. He pulled me along beside him for a few steps and turned to look at me. I don't know if it was the sun, or dust, or a tear, but something made me rub my eye. He looked at me in the strangest way and then he hugged me.

Five o'clock. He is happy. The book is burning within him. He cannot wait to sit down and write. His uncle lives near here, and we'll go there for the evening. We'll have dinner and sit on the roof and cut down more pennies. He'll drink some wine, and we'll leave. Same pattern. He can never stay in one place. He'll be slightly drunk when we leave. And he'll probably fall so he can have an excuse to complain about the pain. By tomorrow, the book, that all-American classic *Friends and Other Strangers,* will no longer exist.

Six-thirty. The house is empty, but the key is under the porch rug. Norman knows where it is; just as he knows everything else—except, perhaps, how very much I enjoy being in a house, a home. A place with memories. I check the cupboards and find enough of a variety to put together a good meal. Norman wanders around in a trance. He seems happy, too. He says he's going out for a bottle of wine. I kiss him goodbye as he leaves. Not goodbye, really; sort of I'll miss you. I put dinner in the oven and go upstairs to shower. Water. Clean water. Chemically treated water from deep underground, without much radioactivity. Not "fresh" water we find in streams and lakes as we travel around. It's good to have clean water instead of "fresh" water for a change.

Seven-thirty. We are alone. Dinner and the wine are quite good. He says my cooking has improved. Good.

Nine o'clock. I had forgotten what a bed was like. Now I remember. He said make love this time. Not screw or fuck. Perhaps he has not changed that much after all. Perhaps we just needed to see the inside of a house or feel the softness of a bed. I can look at him without contempt. I almost feel sorry for all the suffering he does. I think I love him, but I won't admit it. That would spoil the game.

Eleven-thirty. He has told me to get some sleep. We are leaving at five-thirty tomorrow morning. I never want to wake up. I am happy—well, almost happy. I kiss him good night. Pleasant dreams he says. Dreams.

Five-thirty on a Tuesday morning. The dawn tastes different and smells different when you're inside a house. I turn softly so I won't wake him. But he is gone. There is a letter on the pillow.

Wide-awake now. This is no dream. I sit up and read the letter. Kira, it says but I can hardly read it through my tears, Kira believe me it is better this way. What can I say to make you understand that needing me is better than having me? Part of you wants my kind of life; part of you wants security. You have always wanted the security of friends and other strangers, excuse the pun, but you have. If I stayed long enough to talk it over, I'd never leave. We both know that. Goodbye Kira.

The sun is shining now. It shines on the ring that was on the pillow under the letter. I slip it on, covering the white circle that it left. It still fits. Seems like ages since I wore it. It's made from an antique spoon that we found in Massachusetts. It feels cool on my face as I brush away the tears.

At times I will miss seeing you, Norman.

At times.

Reading Between the Words

by Samuel R. Delany

The young painter who has set about learning to paint "realistically" is often surprised that the eye must do the learning; the hand more or less takes care of itself. "But I can *already* see what's there! Tell me what I'm supposed to *do* to get it down."

Keep your hand still and look more closely.

As "realistic" painting does not exhaust art, neither does the comparatively high resolution of narrative story-telling exhaust fiction. But the young writer who has decided to utilize his experience of the world at this comparatively high resolution, for like reasons, is always surprised when he is told to go back and re-examine this experience.

"But I want to know how to write an exciting piece of action!"

Examine your reactions when you are excited; as well, when you are bored.

"But how do I create a vivid character?"

Look closely at what individualizes people; explore those moments when you are vividly aware of a personality. Explore the others when you cannot fathom a given person's actions at all.

"No, no! You don't get the point. Tell me about style!"

Listen to the words that come out of your mouth; look at the words you put on paper. Decide with each whether or not you want it there.

But it will always be a paradox to the young artist of whatever medium that the only element of the imagination that can be consciously and conscientiously trained is the ability to observe what is.

A teacher of narrative fiction fails or succeeds according to the ingenuity with which he can present the above in as many ways as possible—a success or failure that, alas, has nothing to do with his own writing ability.

In speculative fiction, science fiction, or fantasy, the focus on these basics must be even sharper. The substance of sf is still experience (even the experience of the language itself), but at a level of significant distortion—not for any gamelike purpose where the reader tries to reconstruct the "reality," but to generate new experience, a new reality, full and resonant with itself.

Sf is in an exciting aesthetic situation. Essentially intellectual in inspiration, it has a very direct relation with a very large audience, a relation one would be more likely to associate with some performance art (like opera) rather than something so "abstract." It has a maniacally active fandom of several thousands and a knowledgeable audience of several hundred thousands—readers who are literate in traditions which go back to Wells and Verne. Despite nearly a century of conventions, current production is still the most exciting part of the sf experience for most of that audience (unlike opera; indeed, more like rock). Until the last four or five years, this situation was maintained with practically no academic sanction. It is a sign of the field's vitality that among the first college courses established in the subject was the Clarion Workshop, dealing with the writing of sf, the appreciation being taken for granted. It has been quoted many times: "No one reads sf because he has to."

A teacher at Clarion, you may live in the dormitory with the students, or room in a separate building. The students are energetic, dedicated, writing and revising through the six weeks. The solution to most literary problems is time and thought. But if someone can be there immediately to suggest where thought might be directed, so much the better. I chose to room in the student dorm. I had given occasional lectures and one-day seminars; summers ago I had taught remedial reading to a volunteer class at a community center. But Clarion, for five days, was my first formal teaching experience. A handful of the students were older than I. Several had sold stories and novels already.

The situation would intrigue any teacher of fiction.

A writer of fiction, I could not resist it.

The real worth of that summer, as with any intense,

organic experience, is in the texture of the experience itself.

I had set up exercises and discussion topics for the formal, three-hour morning classes. Part of this time was set aside for the group discussion of stories handed in the previous days.

In my first "class," we began by discussing some rather complex ideas about the way information is carried by and between words. We read some sentences, word at a time, to see just what the information given was—tone of voice, mood, order of presentation and importance—and at which points in the sentence this information became apparent. I tried to examine just what happened in the micro-leaps between words. I had notes. But there were great silences in the discussion when I and the students were both at a loss for what to say next. Afterward, I was very relieved when two people came up to discuss ideas of their own that more or less took off from things I had said in class. But even later, when I asked two others, whose comments had seemed the most astute, what they thought of the session, I was cheerfully informed they hadn't the foggiest idea what I was talking about.

And the next morning in class, a girl whose writing had already struck me as among the most talented asked guardedly: "But what do you feel about just pure story-telling?"

I wasn't quite sure what to say, so I came out with: "I like it a whole lot!"

Then we spent five seconds wondering if we should say anything more, and decided on a truce.

An exercise fared better.

I asked the students to choose partners. Limiting themselves to written words (pencil, pen and paper; or typewriter), each was to collect material from the other for a brief biography. "Write a question, exchange papers with your partner; write down your answer to his question (or your comment or request for further explanation of the question), then give the paper back. Read what you've obtained, and write down another question, and continue the process until you feel you have enough information for a short biography. If possible, conduct the experiment without seeing your partner—for example, pass your papers back and forth under a door."

The dorm hall, usually filled in the evening with frisbees and laughter, tonight was oddly quiet. I passed some four couples sitting on the hall floor, exchanging notebooks, and one boy with his typewriter before a closed door, sliding out a sheet of yellow paper.

Several people gave me rather odd looks. One girl, coming out of her room to deliver a paper to a boy in another, asked with somewhat amused belligerence: "Where did you get this idea, anyway?"

Next morning in class, I asked for someone to read his questions and answers. No one raised a hand.

"Someone must have done the exercise," I said. "I saw too many of you working on it."

People shifted in their chairs, glanced at one another.

Momentarily I suspected I was victim of a practical joke.

But when a discussion did, haltingly, begin, it seemed that almost without exception, the twenty-five very bright, very sensitive young people had found, when their communication was limited to the written word, almost in spite of themselves they had shunted into personal areas and intensely emotional parts of themselves that felt uncomfortable before oral display . . . though no one was averse to my or each other's *reading* these papers.

As the discussion progressed, some people volunteered to read sections out loud. Even from this, it became clear that when a one-to-one situation is fixed between information wanted and information granted, with the communicants checking out one another after each step, the result is a strange freedom, an obsessive honesty, a compelling and rising clarity. The general superiority of the prose style to most of their fictional attempts was duly noted.

This was certainly what I had hoped the point of the exercise would be. But I had never tried it in this way. *I* was surprised by the emotional force behind the point.

Another exercise was done in class.

"This morning," I said, "I want you all to look around the room—get up and walk around if you'd like. Observe the people in the room with you, very closely. Keep looking until you notice something about one of your classmates that you've never noticed before. Now examine this thing about him, this aspect of his behavior or appearance, until you see something about it different from the way anyone else you've ever seen exhibits this feature of appearance or behavior. Then write down what you've seen in a sentence or two."

I got in two styrofoam cups of coffee from the urn in the corner while the class milled and prowled by one another. One girl came up to me and said, "But I just don't *see* anything!"

"Make up something," I told her softly, "and see if anyone notices."

Twenty minutes later, most people were seated again. I suggested we bring the class to order and hear some of the examples. If there was any embarrassment here, it was of a lighter tone. Before we started, there was some humorous anticipation of the crashing triviality of what had been observed. But by the third example, the giggles had ceased. People were leaning forward in their chairs, or looking back over their own examples with renewed attention.

If the previous exercise had discovered a lucid, working prose, this one, in example after example, pushed language to the brink of the poetic. The reading, as we went about the room, became a torrent of metaphors—how many of the unique things noted were the resemblance between something present and something else! And those that were not metaphorical still had an astonishing presence, the gesture, expression, or turn of speech caught with the stark economy of the tuned ear, the fixed eye.

There were other discussions on the economic significance of story setting, the natural tendency of words to say things other than you intend and obscure your meaning, and the necessity of rendering your fictional incidents intensely through the senses. When one of my convoluted arguments brought us to a point of confused silence, Robin Wilson, who led the half of the class devoted to story discussion, patiently and kindly extricated me from the snarls of my own inexperience.

The high point of the five days' classes for me was when, after a discussion of the way the vividness of fictional characters usually lies *between* rather than *in* the facts we know of them, one young woman produced a character sketch of an aging, alcoholic midwestern lady with bohemian pretensions. I had asked the class to put together these sketches of fictional characters through a collection of actions—purposeful, habitual, and gratuitous—that should be observed with the same astuteness with which they had observed one another. Unforunately I cannot reproduce the sketch here. But when it was read, among the dozen or so other examples, the class was silent in that way which makes someone who has previously been uproariously applauded feel he has turned, a poor showing after all.

I left Clarion aware just how short five days were—I had actually been on campus five days and two weekends.

Besides the three hours a day of classes, I had read some sixty-five or seventy student stories (and one novel) and had managed at least one story conference with each student—in some cases, with the more prolific, three, four, or five. It was stimulating, intense, even numbing. Most of the students seemed to feel that the individual work with particular stories was the most valuable part of the workshop. The most repeated exchange in these sessions:

"Now in this paragraph/sentence/section here, can you tell me just what you were trying to say?"

Answer. . . .

"Well, I think it would have been better if you'd *said* that. . . ."

In perhaps three or four cases I was able to reassure some people who had worked very hard that the work, at least, was evident. For the rest, I just feel very flattered.

Rilke says in a letter that in the end all criticism comes down to a more or less happy misunderstanding.

I suspect he is right—which is why the literary worth of a workshop like Clarion cannot be defined by simply reviewing what, critically, went on.

The phenomenal percentage of writers from Clarion who have gone on to begin selling sf stories and novels has been mentioned elsewhere. I don't think I am revealing any profound secret by noting that sales has always been a rather distant emblem for quality. It is an emblem here, however, of the field's life, and the openness to new writers, new substance, and new techniques that has characterized it the last five or six years. In this time, sf has been approached from many new directions; the Clarion Workshop is one of the most exciting.

Gerry Conway got his start writing continuity for comic strips and became both the youngest and the best-paid writer in the comic-mystery field. Now he is a prolific writer of fine science fiction; his first novel (Ace) is due to be published shortly. He writes: "The genesis of any story is likely to be nebulous, sounding vague and pointless to all but the writer, for a story, especially one like 'Silent Hands,' will remain highly personal, regardless of its general appeal. 'Silent Hands' was first conceived as the cry of the craftsman desiring to be an artist; it developed into something more. . . ."

Silent Hands

by Gerard F. Conway

It was a cold morning; he could feel the cold in his muscles, tightening in bands across his back and around his waist. He stretched, kneading the small of his back with the knuckles of his left hand as he stepped over Lyrna; she lay curled into a ball on the bed-mat, her legs tucked up to her chest, her arms wound around her knees. She was asleep, calm and relaxed, for a change.

Bending, he dug about in the pile of layout sketches heaped on the low utility table, found the coffee bowl, and pulled it out. He switched it on, lowered himself to the floor, and took up a handful of the sketches, sifting through them while he waited for the coffee to heat, looking for the ones Lyrna had marked for use later that day when they would work on the painting.

She shifted in her sleep, muttered something, twisting around. He prodded her with his foot, roughly. "Get up. Lot to be done. Get up." She pushed his foot away, turned over on her side. Leaning forward, he poked her shoulder. "Said to get up. To get moving."

"Tired. Lemme sleep."

"Uh-uh. We talk. Talk, now." He jabbed her hard in the stomach. She jerked away, sat up.

"What's so damned important." She pushed her hair away from her face, blinked at him with unfocused eyes.

"Talking, classy bitch."

"So, go ahead. Talk." Stretching, she pushed her arms away from her chest, hand clasping wrist, moving with a feline grace. "I'm awake, so talk."

He crossed his legs, settled himself back against a leg

of the utility table. He felt uncomfortable, now that he'd reached the point of saying what was troubling him. Somehow, when it remained unspoken, it remained unrealized. He said, with effort, "Why we no touch? Why we never come together?"

She looked at him, glanced away. "Why bother?"

"No answer, that. Easy words, you say. Not here, no trouble here, no," he patted his chest. "Not here, but in you. I want. I want to touch, but no, you not give me that. Take everything, not even give me that."

"For God's sake—let's not start that whole scene again." She unwound her legs, twisted around and pushed herself to her feet. Hands at hips, she leaned back, unknotting the muscles in her back. "You're the Hand, Karl. Nothing more than the Hand. I can't let a Hand touch me."

"Yeah, you. You think something big, you are. All you do, you take from me. You think you real special."

"And maybe you are? Why should I let you near me, when you couldn't do anything if you wanted?"

"Your fault, bitch. You like ice, so cold you burn hand. Can't touch you way you are, can't do nothing but paint picture for you—and that's nothing. Oh, shove." He punched the floor, closed his eyes, and pressed himself back against the table leg; he found it difficult to speak, to put his feelings into words. That was part of the problem between them, but not all of it; he felt helpless, useless.

She looked at him for a moment, turned away, and went over to the large, rumpled sofa by the door. Sitting, she drew her legs up, peered at him over her knees.

"I had a dream last night," she said, slowly. "In it I was groping for something, something I couldn't quite touch, couldn't get my hands around. It was the painting. I kept seeing it, and drawing close to it, but I could never put my hands on it."

"Tough," he said. "Real tough, huh."

"I was alone, and I knew that if I just had someone else there, I could see and feel the damned thing all at once. I could become part of it, completely. But there was no one, and there would never be any one." She looked down at him. "And that's how it feels to be an Eye."

"Real classy bitch, you. Real starlet bitch. But you never go nowhere without your Hand, huh? Never be able do any painting without Hand." The bowl hissed; the coffee was ready. He turned away from her, set the layouts down, and pulled a cup from the dispenser. "Damn it. Damn it all straight." He poured out a cup for himself. "Coffee?"

"No."

Setting the bowl for warming, he pushed it back under the sketch pile. It continued to hum softly, an undertone to their words.

"Tell one thing, classy bitch. Tell—why me? Why you pick me? Maybe there more than just Hand, huh? Maybe classy starlet see something in Hand she not tell herself, huh?"

"Don't kid yourself, Karl. You've got something I need. I don't have to like you for it, and I don't. I don't think about you at all—you're my Hand. That's all. Everything you could be is gone, everything you ever were is gone, everything. You're my Hand." She shifted, pulled down an edge of skirt. "The only thing that matters between us is the painting. That's all. The sooner we get that straight, the stronger we'll be together. The painting, Karl."

"And you dream about painting."

"And I dream about the painting. It's all I have to dream about."

"Got plenty else to do in bed though, huh, classy bitch?"

"Trick questions? What's that supposed to mean?"

"Think Karl really dumb, blind in eye like in art? Think he don't see you go out, get laid? Think Karl really dumb, don't you?"

She didn't say anything; she uncrossed her legs, set them down straight before her, smoothing her skirt with a cross-down motion of her hand.

"Good," he said. He drank off his coffee, threw the empty cup across the room. "Really good. Blind Hand, Blind Eye . . . really good. Chop-chop, pick-pick. Just pick at scabs, just pick, and pick, and pick." He bowed his head, looked up again, smiling. "You kill us both, classy bitch. You kill us both."

She nodded. Outside the window, the morning mist was beginning to clear.

Later that day, he slept, and dreamed of dark corridors and blind, groping hands. He awoke, dripping with sweat. The bedclothes were wound in tangles around his legs, bunched up under his spine, soaked through; he pushed them away, sat up.

Lyrna was gone. A note perched on a plate of prepared meat-jellies told him she'd gone to pick up some supplies for the painting that afternoon. He crumpled the note, dropped it in the disposal unit behind the table, took up the plate of jellies, and went over to the window seat. Settling himself against the wall, he stared out into the day mist, letting his thoughts run. The jellies were tart, only half-convincing in their attempt to taste like roast beef.

Everything between them had come together in a month; the meeting, the teaming, all the petty jealousies, all the strife, everything that had been picking away at their private wounds; all of it, one month, had come together when he found her with that Engineer from the in-system shuttle. It was something he'd suspected, but which he'd never let himself accept, until it was thrust upon him, blatantly, callously. She hadn't even cared that he'd found out. He mattered so little to her that it didn't even bother her that she'd hurt him.

He felt useless, emasculated. As an art team, creating paintings, they worked together flawlessly; but on a personal level, they couldn't mesh . . . everything they did seemed to cut them. Every word, every action; pick-pick, pulling off the crust of the old wounds.

He took up a handful of meat-jelly, bit off a mouthful.

She couldn't see what she did to him; she couldn't let herself see.

They were alone. Together, they were alone.

The jellies were really quite sour. He put them down, pushed them away across the window seat. He wasn't hungry any more.

"You pretty long, huh?"

"No." She turned away from him, set the packages down on the table, squaring them against each other, carefully, nervously. She straightened, brushed back a lock of hair from her face, started to unbutton her rain-slick. He reached out, stopped short of grabbing her arm, took the coat instead. She didn't look around at him.

"Two hours not long to find supplies?"

"I had to go across town. Everything isn't right here, you know."

"Two hours."

"Yes, two hours." She swung away, busied herself with unpacking the supplies, setting the small paint knives and brushes in even little rows along a cleared-off section of the table.

"Your hands shake. Why lie to me, huh? Why bother kid me? Why we do this, why hurt, why hack?"

"Shut up." She steadied her hands, arranged the palette, started opening up the jars of paint.

"Sure, he shut up. No Eyes, why should he have mouth, right?"

No answer.

He stared at her a moment, then turned away, looked down at his hands, back up at the blank wall across from him. Finally, he turned back, moved in to help her unpack.

They finished eating in silence, and while he cleaned up the few undisposable dishes, Lyrna went about the preparations for the painting. She brought out the thick, lightly painted plasticanvas, set it into place on the easel, straightened it until it was just right, and then snapped the locks into place. She gathered up the tools from the table, arranged them on the small shelf of the easel, filled the brushes and honed the knives, scraped the palette and left it on the tiny table next to the pillows in front of the easel. She moved quickly, efficiently, but without the grace that would have allowed her to work her own brushes; watching her, he saw the little defects in motion—the short, clipped forward movements, the nervous sideways flutter, the tendency to push rather than guide a piece of material. It was in her face, as well: her jawline was tense, strained. One word: nervous.

He waited until she was done, and then he took his place in front of the easel, easing down onto the pillows, closing his eyes. He heard her settle onto the paddings behind him, heard the rustle of cloth against cloth as she curled herself into a comfortable position. He let the tension pass down out of his arms, through his hands and out of his fingers; he could feel it, a physical release. He repeated this forced relaxation with his chest, his stomach, his legs, his feet: all the tension, out. He drew blank, empty; he saw white dappled with gray, floured with patches of suntouched yellow, cool, warm, cool again. His mind softened its hold, opened wide.

Behind him: Lyrna.

Her hands touched his shoulders, rose to his neck, pressed gently under his ears. He could hear the blood pounding in his skull, through her hands and into his skull, out of his skull, into her: her mind entered his.

Two:

One.

One:

Two.

One: One.

They opened their eyes and saw the canvas, the whole canvas, the texture of the plasticloth, the depth and grain of the material, the pores, the rivers of design, the paint crusting over the canvas, digging deeply into the canvas, becoming a part of the canvas: the design.

They saw the canvas, the design: the curves down the right and left, the straight, parallel bars in the center, the symmetry and the balance of the colors; all of it coming together in the Design—for it was larger now in their eyes, much larger; it was art, and they were creating it, creating it as she brought his Hand up and guided it with her mind, their mind, and the brush dabbed out, stroking slowly down—

NO!

He thrust her away, her mind out of his mind, and he held the brush in his own hand, made a slash across the canvas, followed it with another slash, cut those with a third, again and again, spilling paint across the art, twisting and forcing himself forward toward the canvas, fighting the hysterical pull of her mind, her silent screams in his silent ears. He fought off her mental hold, took the brush and cut, had to cut, to make it part of *him*, part of Karl, not just his Hands but his soul; not just a craftsman holding a tool but an artist holding his soul and wielding it as a knife in a surgeon's hand; he wanted to make her see, to make her understand—

And he cut.

And he tore at the art they'd made;

Ripped it.

Destroyed it.

His hands were his own, but he hadn't the grace to control them.

After a time of this, an endless, cruel time of madness, he fell away from the murdered canvas, and lay still.

She was watching him when he awoke. She'd been cry-ing; her eyes were red, ridged with brown marks where her make-up had run. She was holding the canvas to her. One hand clutched a crossbar on the back, trembling spasmodically; twitching and jumping as it fought to hold the fiber glass.

"Why?" she asked.

"You couldn't see. You saw everything else—but no see me."

"I . . . don't . . . know . . ."

"No. Classy bitch, wouldn't know. I was Hand. Nothing more to you. Not someone who felt . . . who burned. Who hurt for failings of self as you hurt for yours. You not see me. Wouldn't."

Her head dropped forward, lay sideways, cheek against the frame of the painting.

"I wanted paint, Lyrna. Wanted to See, as you Saw." The words came slowly, but there was time, enough time to say them right. "Couldn't. Can't, ever. But that not hurt as much as what you did, classy bitch. Left me cold; could have helped, have shared as I share with you my Hands . . . but never would. Kept it for yourself, and hated me for what I gave you.

"I was your Hand . . . but you never was my Eye."

She lifted her head slowly from the painting, stared at him. One of her hands came up.

"Help me?"

He rose, went over to her, took the hand. Touching. Holding briefly. Her hand was cold. His hand was cold.

Silent hands.

Steve Herbst is a twenty-year-old Chicagoan with long hair and even longer thoughts. He has a trick of pinning down some of the more ephemeral—but no less painful—aspects of the human condition. Of this story, he writes: "When you don't know, you don't know, you know? And it can eat your heart out. The main character in this story isn't necessarily an all-time loser; he's just having a bad day." Here is a portrait of the ten percent who never quite get the word.

An Uneven Evening

by Steve Herbst

Peter's back had been bothering him again; when he reached for the newspaper on a nearby table, he stiffened. There was no crick of pain this time. I am swiftly becoming an old man, he told himself.

"Peter, how's your back feeling?"

"It's all right."

Nancy read her *McCall's* on the sofa, ignoring the television set, which she had turned on to play the early evenings news. She seemed content to keep her body still and move only her eyes. The magazine's pastel advertisements held her attention completely.

My wife is a boring woman, Peter thought. See how her fat face never alters its expression. See how her body rests slackly against the cushions and how her arms lie at her sides. See how the magazine on her lap is her evening plaything. See how I am left to fill a chair silently and become boring also.

And how boring I feel, he thought. What an incapable person I am. A dead weight suited to living-room chairs. On Wednesday nights I hit pool halls and drink beer, for of that am I capable. That is, when I ride in the car with Teague and Marvin Sapello. With Marvin and Teague I am a functioning organism, but when I am home I fill chairs.

Peter filled his chair and read his paper until the doorbell rang, to his great relief. Teague and Marvin came into the living room after wiping their feet on the floor mat.

"You look bored, old buddy," said Marvin jovially and lowered himself into a chair.

"Hey, hey," Teague said at the same time, sagging against a wall and hanging his jaw. "Ready to go?"

My evening of boredom, Peter thought, is giving way to one of virile entertainment. I now reject studied inactivity and uneasy introspection for the security of my friends, old games, and a more forceful and satisfying social role. An escape from air-conditioned purgatory into culturally competitive paradise.

"Fuckin' mellow," he said. He hit Teague in the arm. "Let's get out of here."

They were in Teague's small Plymouth, Teague and Peter in front and Marvin in the back. Peter looked out the window. He kept his lips pressed tightly together as usual, betraying a minimum of emotion.

"How many games we gonna play tonight, eh?" Teague smiled, looking straight ahead into traffic.

"We can play until the owner throws us out," Marvin answered, his cheeks bulging when he talked. "Wear us out a pool table, ain't that right?"

"Yup," said Peter.

Teague drove impatiently, barely avoiding the night people in the streets, watching his headlight beams play on storefronts when he turned corners. His big arms rested fully on the steering wheel most of the time; he seemed to be embracing the car and the power it gave him.

"I told Willie Amberay and Sam Orr I'd pick them up. We're gonna fill the car tonight, hey," said Teague.

So he pulled up at Sam Orr's house and ran up to ring the doorbell. Sam and Willie were outside immediately, loping down the stairs side by side. They got into the back seat, craning their necks and darting their eyes about.

"Hi, Pete. Marvin."

"What's up?" said Peter.

Sam pulled the door closed and Teague pulled away abruptly. Willie lit a cigarette, scenting the inside of the car.

"*Hey*, Teague, guess what we found out today," Sam began.

"Yeah?"

"Get this, there's a new torming hall just opened on East Andrew Street, they got twenty-five tubes and strong alignment. What do you think of *that?*"

"Twenty-five, huh? Pretty neat, y'know?"

"Listen, Teague, if you and everybody wants to go there tonight instead of the same old pool game? Huh?"

Peter wasn't at all sure that he had heard that exchange correctly. What was Sam talking about, "torming"? What kind of term was that?

But Teague seemed to know.

"That's fine with me," Marvin said. "I haven't shot rings in, oh, a long time. Are they full-sized fields, do you know?"

"Yeah, right," said Willie. "Ten rings, oh, maybe sixty degrees up and down. That's what I heard."

"Shit, man, fuck," exclaimed Sam gloriously. "It's been so long. So long. Get the old form back, long dives, everything. Jesus!" He waved his arms in the air, grinning. "Jesus, such a long time."

Peter began to worry. What in hell was torming? He considered asking and admitting his stupidity.

"Hey, Pete," called Teague. "A good torm okay with you? We'll let the pool go tonight."

Peter decided to play it cool. "Yeah, great. How far is the place?"

"Oh, a few blocks down Andrew. I think fourteen hundred east."

Peter nodded and turned his gaze back out the window. He was just the least bit worried.

The outside of the torming hall was a storefront with a small sign—TORMING/25 TUBES—printed in neon. Then an unobtrusive doorway, and then a long escalator going down. Peter and his friends filed in neatly and descended to the front lobby.

The lobby was surprisingly big and modern. Gleaming metal arches spaced every twenty feet around the ellipsoidal room soared upward to a ceiling maybe fifty feet high. Carpeting on the floor and on walls between the arches was light-green and very thick. The pattern of metal and green was unbroken on all sides, except for washroom portals and a food concession at one end of the ellipse, and a counter set in the wall at the other end. The carpeting helped to absorb the noise made by the hall's patrons and by a powerful air-conditioning system. A fragrant odor filled the place, and bright fluorescents overhead illuminated every square inch evenly.

Peter and his friends were standing in front of a long, polished desk in the center of the room behind which were banks of tiny lights, knob controls, and two receptionists. Teague murmured, "I've gotta use the john; get us a tube, okay?" Teague and Sam left.

Peter tried to hang back, hoping that either Marvin

or Willie would take care of any arrangements. But, un-
fortunately, he found himself up against the desk, and
one of the receptionists asked him, "Yes?"

He thought fast. If this place was anything like a bowling alley, then he was supposed to reserve a lane. Or, in
this case, a *tube*.

"A tube?" he said casually, and the receptionist handed
him a bulky plastic key with number 5 embossed on it.
Peter wasn't sure whether there was anything else to ask
for, but the girl said, "Get belts over there," and she
pointed with her arm toward the opposite end of the lobby.

Belts?

Marvin and Willie were already at the belts counter, and
Peter watched the man behind the counter select their sizes
and hand them belts. So he went to the man and asked for
a belt, got a belt, and put the belt around his waist.

The belt was heavy plastic half a foot wide and it had
weights built into it. Three weights, evenly spaced around
him.

What could the belt be for? A handicap of some sort? A
thing to hold equipment? Peter walked as easily as possible under the added weight, trying to look as if nothing
was new to him.

"What number, Pete?" asked Marvin.

Peter announced the number and said, "Where do you
suppose that would be, eh?"

Marvin pointed toward the back side of the lobby and
said, "Over there, probably."

At least Marvin didn't know everything for sure.

When they had walked behind the lobby, what Peter
saw completely took his breath from him.

"Oh, no. OH, no."

They were standing on a balcony. In front of them the
floor dropped a hundred and fifty feet in a long, slow
curve. Fluorescent lights at the top of the huge torming
room illuminated the smoke-filled air and set off dramatically the distance between balcony and floor, between
balcony and opposite wall. Along this distance, down a
seventy-three-degree angle, stretched the tubes.

"What was that, Pete?"

"Oh, uh, they're fuckin' small, that's what. Don't you
think?"

"Regulation size, I dunno," said Willie.

The tubes were rows of ten soft plastic hoops about six
feet across, and looking through them one could see the

far diagonal end of the chamber. The tubes were a couple of hundred feet long.

But that wasn't the worst of it, Peter saw.

People were torming in the tubes.

All down the line, men, women, children were leaping with abandon head first into the upper ends of the tubes and with their arms pressed against their sides, they were falling through the hoops. As they fell they collided with the hoops and glanced off. On and on, fast, ricocheting down and disappearing at the bottom.

"Did you get an egg, Pete?" Willie said, examining knob controls by the side of tube number 5.

Peter looked wildly about the room, back into the lobby, to find a place to get eggs. He couldn't see any counter besides the one for belts, nor anything that should be called an egg. What was an egg?

"Here, these guys have one," said Marvin, and he walked over to the tube numbered 7 where three small children and their parents were torming. The children jumped into the rings fearlessly, touched several times, and disappeared at the bottom of the tubes, while a conspicuous green display registered a number from zero to ten beside the topmost ring.

The "egg" was resting on the floor behind them. Marvin asked the father of the family, and then he stooped to pick up the egg. The egg was a light, foot-long metal ellipsoid, perfectly featureless except for a hole in one end. After turning the tube on with the numbered key, Willie took the egg and centered it in the topmost ring; a magnetic field drew it to the exact center and held it there. When Willie reversed a switch, the egg dropped slickly down the tube.

"A little too far to the left, I think," said Willie.

"Aligned pretty well, I'd say. Just a touch off."

"Too far to the left," Peter said with conviction.

So Willie played with two knobs until the path of the egg satisfied him. Then he said quickly, "Who wants to go first?"

Peter nearly panicked when he thought about jumping into the rings and practically free-falling two hundred feet head down. Very nearly panicked. He couldn't see what was down at the bottom of the huge room, but he did see the tormers come up each time through doors in the floor. He tried to assure himself that if he were to jump into the tube, he too would come up through a door in the floor.

"Wait for Teague and Sam," he said.

"Is it aligned?" Teague asked when he came back.
"Fairly well," said Willie.
"Well then, go ahead."

Willie stepped up to the tube without a word, tossed his watch and car keys to Teague, and leaped gracefully down the tube. He touched four times and then they lost sight of him. The exhibition took a little under two seconds. Then it was Marvin's turn.

Marvin slicked back his hair, waved his meaty arms, and dove in. He collided right away with the third ring, which event threw him off balance and caused him to touch five more times on the way down. At this point Willie came up through the floor.

Now it was Peter's turn.

My friends are unafraid, thought Peter. That, at least, has been proved to my satisfaction. Also, this is a fancy establishment. I think it is amazingly strange, but definitely fancy. Also there are children falling down the tubes, and none of them is getting hurt, and no one is worrying about them. Therefore, in all probability, I am perfectly safe.

What I must be concerned with, then, is being skillful. The score is based on the number of rings touched, that much is clear. If a person's aim is accurate initially, he will touch fewer rings. If his corrections are adequate when he touches a ring, he will touch fewer rings afterward. What I must do is . . .

"Go, Pete," said Sam. "It looks to be aligned all right from the way Willie went."

Skill, Peter realized, should not concern him in the least until he had satisfied himself about the matter of safety. He realized also that he wasn't satisfied. He was still scared to death.

"Don't you want to take your watch off?"

He took off his watch.

He held his breath involuntarily and jumped into the tube.

The dive was a bad one. He hit the second ring at the top of its curve, solidly, and it bounced him off and sent him spinning. The tube's magnetic field swung him around and he found himself soaring up into space, outside the rings. He flew straight up, head over heels, terror-stricken, until a secondary field caught him and fastened him on the ceiling.

"No!" he cried, trying to sound as annoyed as possible

instead of scared. He looked down dizzily at the floor below.

"Grab a hand rail!" Sam called. Teague was coming up through the floor and when he saw Peter on the ceiling, he burst out laughing.

"Hey, that's pretty neat," he chuckled.

Peter found a railing and pulled himself back to the balcony. He dropped down to the carpeted floor. "Yeah," he smiled, checking his heavy breathing. His miscalculation had been an honest one, he realized, one for which he would not be ostracized.

"Try again, man."

No, not again, he thought. "Yeah," he said. "Yeah." He grinned.

No, no. He hopped in more gingerly this time, plummeted into the third ring, and clung to it for dear life. Below him seven more rings hovered vertiginously against the pale-green background of carpet a hundred feet down. He crawled along the rim of the ring, then, to face toward the middle. Stretching his hands in front of him and letting go with his feet, he fell, and hit every remaining ring on the way down.

A long curved ramp and a magnetic field stopped him at the bottom. As he lay sprawled on the wide, smooth floor, he saw a series of conveyors curving upward and disappearing into the walls. He stepped onto one. The ride was quick. At the top, a trap door opened and he was lifted onto the main-floor balcony in time to see Teague drop off into a three-touch fall.

"You okay, Pete?"

"Yeah, Marvin. What's wrong?"

"An eight-point, shit!" said Sam. "Outa practice, huh?"

"Yeah, maybe," he answered. "Field isn't, uh, very strong, is it?"

"Strongest field I've been in, myself."

"Yeah."

Peter made a seven-touch the next time and flew around the outside of two rings on the way. He came up through the door in the floor and wrote "7" on his score sheet. Willie caught his error and explained to him: "You went outside on the way down, Pete. Twice."

"Yeah, right."

"That's an extra two points, you know. Tryin' to cheat yourself?"

Peter made the correction, and Willie asked, "You ever do a torm before, Pete? Honest now."

"Asshole! You think I'm trying to impress somebody or something?" He grinned, slapping Willie on the back.

"I know," said Willie in a low voice, "that you tend to do that."

Peter lined up his next jump carefully, sighting all the way down and then listing forward in what he thought was a professional-looking posture. He swung his arms to take off, and a muscle went in his back.

He went tense from the momentary cramp, stiffened from head to foot, and fell seven rings without touching.

When he hit bottom he turned over once and stopped short on his knees, still tensed. An older man lay near him on the floor, and before he could get up the man called to him.

"Are you hurt?"

"No, shit, I'm all right." Peter smiled coolly.

"Well, *I'm* hurt," the man said, and propped himself up on one knee.

Peter helped the man to the up conveyor while the man explained. "I've got a trick knee, see, and I got it locked up on the way down. No fault of the equipment, understand. The equipment's perfectly safe."

Peter remembered that afterward. The equipment's perfectly safe.

The man thanked him when they reached the torming balcony above and a place to sit down. Peter said, "It's all right," and left to get his wrist watch from tube 5's scoring desk.

I am a very misdirected person, he thought. I waste my energies. I find no joy in social paradise.

He said good night to all his friends, gave them some money for the torming, returned his belt, and took the bus home.

He found his wife still reading *McCall's* on the sofa. The television was still on, and the late evening news was playing. He waited for a greeting from her; anything, but she ignored him and continued to read the magazine.

Finally, he volunteered: "It was okay, we had fun."

She turned a page and continued to read.

"Nan?"

"Yes, Peter?" She looked up.

"Are you watching television? I'm going to shut it off."

"Go right ahead, I'm not watching." She returned to the page.

Peter watched her in the silent room for a long time,

thinking about boring evenings and dull purgatories and culturally competitive paradises and wives.

And then his face brightened up all at once. He went over to Nancy on the sofa, bent over her from behind with his hands on her shoulders and his face close to hers.

He said, "Hey, honey, tomorrow night I'm going to take you torming."

She looked up this time.

"Oh. Great," she said. "Strong alignment?"

Evelyn Lief is an attractive little woman about the size of my fourteen-year-old daughter. She has been writing professionally now for about two years, and she gets better and better. This story combines reality of detail with a surrealist background that is becoming all too familiar; it is a combination that Evelyn does very well.

The Inspector

by Evelyn Lief

It was dangerous to walk in the street because the weeds hid the deep holes in the torn pavement. The sidewalk buckled upward at the crack, forming a high ridge. She stepped over it and down into a narrow valley of tall grass and daisies.

She wore a green velvet jacket and pants. Tight cuffs around the ankle were in style this year. Tall and thin, not even skin and bones but just bones, she carried a tiny pearl purse in her left hand, and with her other hand kept brushing the red hair away from her eyes.

She walked through one doorway. Yes, this is the right shop. Two steps down, turn to the right, and stoop under a low arch into the small room. It was so quiet she could hear a bird chirping somewhere outside. The floor sounded hollow under her footsteps. She walked around the counter to the far right-hand corner. Strips of wood and one large brick lay in a pile. Carefully, so she wouldn't get dust on her clothes, she pushed away one piece of wood, and then another. But the brick was too heavy for one hand and a gentle push. Leaning over, she picked up the brick, carried it a few inches and had to drop it. The brick scraped the fleshy part of the hand under the thumb.

"Ouch." She licked the blood that began to ooze from the scratched skin. It tasted like wet sawdust.

Then she saw what she had been looking for in the shop. But it was only a piece—one arm of a fat-bellied statue of Buddha. She picked it up.

"Take it if you want."

Her shoulders shook as she dropped the arm and turned around. "I was only looking."

"You can take it. Everything belongs to everyone."

In the dim shop she could only see a dark shape. Dave?

In the middle of the night Dave got up from bed. She had to focus her eyes many seconds before she could even see the outline of his body. She wanted to be at home, in her own small bedroom where no one could hurt her. "Don't leave me," she said.

"I'm here," Dave said. He held the cigarette in his hand as he leaned over the bed to kiss her on the forehead. "And I want you to stay with me."

In the morning he might think she was stupid or ugly. She was afraid to take the chance.

"Will you?" Dave asked.

"Yes, I think I will," she said.

"Come on out and I'll show you around," the Inspector said.

She followed him out the door and stood for a moment, slightly blinded in the sunlight.

When she could see, she saw an old man dressed in khaki shredding at the cuffs and seams, and bent over a walking stick that was too short for him. His long tangled hair fell unevenly over his back and sometimes twisted in front of his face into his beard. Dave had been much younger.

She began to walk away from him.

"Hey, don't be afraid. I'm only the poor old Inspector. They would tell you how harmless I am, if only they were still here." He waved his arms at the crumpled buildings on either side of the street.

His eyes were small, squinting, and she thought that he probably needed glasses. She wanted to talk to someone. "Who were they?"

"All the kids who went to school, or came in the summer to bang out the copper jewelry, or passed around the joints, or worked part-time in the dress shops and cafés, or just hung around until the action started. What's your name?"

"Paula."

"Mine's Dave." He leaned over the counter, resting on

his elbows. His hair was blond and curled in ringlets at
the nape of the neck. A strip of rawhide was tied above
his left elbow.

"How do you like the shop?" Dave asked.

"I love the Buddhas. But they're so expensive." She
shook her head quickly to make her hair fall back behind
her shoulders.

"How would you like to have a cup of coffee with me,
Paula? I can meet you outside the shop in an hour."

"I don't think so."

"Why not?"

"I don't even know you."

"That's a New Yorker speaking." He stopped leaning
on the counter, but continued to look at her. Then he
smiled and said, "I'd give you a Buddha free if I could.
But I can't. So take me instead."

Paula smiled too. "I'm not sure if that's a good trade.
But all right."

"You'll have a chance to find out."

She wondered if she should meet him. But she knew
that she would be waiting outside the shop.

Paula and the Inspector walked away from the shop.
"My name's Paula. Why did they call you the Inspector?"

"Before the bombing, when everything was still happening, I knew everybody. Kind of kept an eye on their business. It was useful in case I got myself in a jam with the
pigs. You know, gave them a little info, and in return
they didn't hassle me too much. I never told them anything
really important."

"Like what?"

"Like, that's the corner where Cynthia used to sit.
Every week or two she'd run out of bennies, and she'd
leave the kid at home or park it in someone's lap. Then
she'd walk up and down the street looking for a handout.
If she didn't get it, Cynthia would just sit herself down
on that corner and wait. If someone didn't slip her one
after a while, I'd tell the pigs and they'd take her in for
the night."

That night three years ago had been her last night with
Dave. She had been afraid of losing him and afraid of
trying to stop him. The kids were going to do it one day.
But Dave had to try to talk to them.

Early in the morning he had gone over to the campus.

"Let's walk over to the campus," the Inspector said.

She never saw Dave again. Five buildings were destroyed.

Only part of one wall of the main visitor's building was still standing. There were piles of rocks sticking out of the high weeds.

One afternoon she and Dave had sat in front of this building, on the steps near the tree with the circling bench. A guitar player strummed softly; two or three people listened. A girl wearing no shoes, tight shorts, and a low blouse without bra began leaping around the tree. The tune became a Russian folksong, lively and quick. Her body was loose as she invested all her energy in the dance.

A police car drove up to the tree. The girl stood panting, the guitar player stopped. There was no more music the rest of the afternoon.

Paula kicked dirt off the stair. The students had been angry and now nothing remained but rubble.

Nothing but rubble and Dave caught under the rocks. Nothing at home but a meaningless job in the hospital and two affairs that hadn't lasted. She had been afraid to care.

She moved her hand through the white smoke and there was nothing. She leaned against the side of the wall. She climbed over the jagged bricks, to the other side that still smoked from the bombing. Her feet burned and her hands were rubbed raw and bloody. Where was Dave? Why didn't he help her?

Why hadn't she stopped him?

Paula sat down on the dirt-covered step.

The Inspector leaned on his stick. "What's wrong?"

"This place is so depressing. We destroyed ourselves."

"It wasn't my fault. It was the pigs. Don't fool yourself. They were out to get us."

"I know. But we helped. I helped Dave die."

She looked at the Inspector and saw the top of his cheeks where they began to cave in under his beard. How many had he helped?

They walked back to Telegraph Avenue, down the street to a little place that said Saloon on a tilted wood sign.

"It's pretty clean in here," the Inspector said. "Do you want some cider? There's still some in the barrel."

"No. Thanks."

"Well, if you don't want that, how would you like to see this?" The Inspector reached down and opened the zipper of his pants. He grabbed her hand. "Just touch."

"No." His fingers were slippery with sweat. Like Dave's on top of the mountain. "Let go. I don't want to." She pulled her hand back, and he let her go.

"I just thought you might. Like in the old days."

Dave had been exciting. She remembered trying to bite his neck, twisting their legs and arms around one another in impossible positions. Laughing. That had been good.

She picked up the arm of the Buddha and began to walk back down Telegraph Avenue. The Inspector followed. "I'm sorry," she said, "but I want to be alone."

"I understand," he said. He stood still, leaning on his walking stick and half smiling, watching her walk down the street.

Just before she entered the shop she turned around to see the Inspector, to see him still standing in the same place on the damaged sidewalk.

First she had to go under the alcove, and then into the dark shop. Paula tried to imagine Dave's body, and saw an old man bent over a walking stick. She tried to see his face, but there were only the squinting eyes and hollow skin under the Inspector's beard.

Where was Dave? She curled up on the floor, next to the counter, not worrying this time about the dust that would cover her clothes. For a few minutes she hugged her knees and the piece of statue on her lap. Finally she stood up and put the wooden arm on the counter.

She brushed her hair away from her eyes and said, "I don't think I can afford it."

When she left the shop the Inspector was gone.

Genre

by JOANNA RUSS

Science fiction is often spoken of as a genre, but genre-hood isn't something we ought to wish on the field. Genre successes are "minor classics" at best (*A Coffin for Demetrios*), while major works—or even just pretentious works—are instantly removed from the body of genre work by reviewers, critics, most readers, and even authors. (If it's good, it can't be science fiction.) Nor is this entirely tendentious.

Genre writing insists on and presupposes certain limitations in what's to be treated and how—not stylizations or conventions, which are open-ended, but genuinely constricting sets of expectations. (I use "convention" here to mean a manner of representing something. The convention does not dictate what is to be represented nearly so narrowly as do the restrictions of genre. "Love at first sight," for example, can be either a convention—in which case it points to something beyond itself—or part of a genre. One is the means, the other the end.) Anybody reading westerns or going to western movies knows that what makes these works "westerns" is the limit on themes, moods, setting, characters, events, place, and time, and that none of these elements can be changed without removing the work from the genre altogether. Genre restrictions work from the outside in—they control the kind of material that can be covered—while what we might call *literary conventions* are structural devices, organizing devices, that work from the inside out—for example, the dramatic soliloquy. Conventions can be used or transcended, but genre restrictions can only be parodied.

People enjoy strict genre writing because of what is left out. Samuel Z. Arkoff's beach movies are a good case in point. Nineteen-year-old boys (his audience, according to an interview with him in *Life* some years ago) don't like to be reminded of the draft, sex, love, death, hate, parents, tragedy, childhood, or work. So all these are left out of beach movies. Very little remains. (Anybody could make this sort of analysis of written genre work: comedy in horror stories, for example, or sex in sword-and-sorcery.)

The interests served by genre writing are often para-literary, e.g. the intellectual puzzle of the "classic" detective story. In all genres, readers look for extra-literary satisfactions—moral, emotional and otherwise—but we all do that in most of what we read.

Genre writing has two faults: staleness and constriction. The first is accidental, but the second is essential; bad writers spend their lives within a genre, deviating just enough from the strict limits to make their works interesting as deviations—e.g. a "different" western, a "different" musical—while good writers either use genre stories as way-stations in their own development or dabble in such stories from time to time, as many great nineteenth-century writers did in their minor works. Once somebody really good has "transcended" a genre—that is, found it undeveloped and given it its final expression—that genre is dead, and not all the efforts of second- to tenth-rate writers can bring it to life again. Staleness becomes unavoidable. One might argue that genres aim from their beginning at artistic extinction: the absolutely rigid, perfectly set story, in which nothing ever varies. Genre worlds have a lot in common with a "secondary universe" as it's customarily defined (in practice if not in theory), an elaborate fantasy world whose unimportant details have become what really matters, e.g. the Baker Street Irregulars argue forever about Holmes's left-hand boot. (This begins to look a little like socially shared paranoid.) What matters in art is what is individual; what matters in genre composition is to avoid deviating in any important way from the prescribed rules. Whole genres have sprung from one or two books, like the modern Gothic, daughter of *Jane Eyre*, or the classic detective puzzle, grandson of Edgar Allan Poe. What is striking is how the genre diminishes its source—that is, there is much less in *The Columbella* and its sisters than in *Jane Eyre;* ditto for Poe and Agatha Christie. When a writer of the first rank exhausts an already-existing genre, his successors can only fail or leave it alone; compare Sheridan LeFanu with

Lovecraft and Lovecraft with the latest Unspeakable Horrors on the newstands.

Great literary successes are not genre stories; they make their own limitations and they walk through existing ones. That is, they live from the inside out. They are organic. H. G. Wells, often called the progenitor of science fiction, was not a genre writer at all; he preceded the genre. Of course it's a matter of historical accident what kinds of imaginary worlds (that is, stories) become rigidified enough to be called genre writing. People read, and pay for, what interests them; stories begin to resemble one another; fidelity to detail becomes of major importance; the whole thing freezes, and there you are. Current science fiction—by this I mean the body of work people refer to when they say "Hey! Science fiction!" (which is Randall Jarrell's "definition by ostentation"; as he says, "You point.")—shows signs of being a genre and of also becoming a convention. The largest genre within science fiction is space opera, i.e. the man's adventure story (a commercial label). The next largest is the emotionless scientific puzzle (a more direct descendant of Wells and Verne). The best of science fiction—the things we in the field call "classics"—are often puzzle or problem stories in which the hero's life is put in danger in order that he shall have a motive for solving the puzzle.

This is bad. The best-known "science-fiction" writer in this country, a man read even by people who don't read science fiction, is Ray Bradbury, a writer who completely disregards the barriers of genre. Whatever constrictions his writing is subject to are not the constrictions of genre. He walks in and out of *that* as if it didn't exist.

It shouldn't.

Until now the best writing in science fiction has been done by people outside the field. They have either appropriated certain attitudes (the impersonal drama of evolution, the impersonal tragedy of entropy) or grand, organizing metaphors (the future as unrealized potential) or they have treated the field as a hoard of fascinating smaller metaphors: robots as people, artificial intelligences as souls, overpopulation as oversocialization, space travel as spiritual travel, biological evolution as meaningfulness, and so on—all of these holding together as attitude and metaphor, that is as structural principles or ways of thinking, not as the imposed limits of a genre. More and more works are being written this way.

There are certain reasons to continue writing in artistically dead territory; to enjoy oneself by retelling the familiar, to make money, to ring interesting changes on something everybody already knows, to write with little effort, to satisfy one's extra-literary interests without having to wrestle with real subject matter, or to cut one's baby teeth. Only the last reason is a good one. Why do what has already been done, especially when it has already been done as well as possible? You can't "infuse" a dead form with life. Its form *is* its life.

Science fiction has been misconceived as a genre from the very beginning, at least in the United States. The best works have never been part of the two genres; they have used genre attitudes and props for their own ends. More than that, readers' interest has always been in what is *new* in a story—a direct contravention of genre ideals. Real attempts to deal with the consequences of change are not confined to science fiction today. This mode of thought is far more important than the minutiae of technical puzzles or the ritualized gestures of heroic adventure, far more interesting, far more poetic, and far more real. Good works have been written this way and great works can be.

The genre must die before it can become real art.

Science-fiction writers can extrapolate more than social and technological themes. Here is a literary cliché extended to its ultimate and very funny conclusion.

Thurston writes: "In movies, especially old movies, melodrama always provides the convenient resolutions. The bad guys will be wiped out, and love will end in reunion or final parting, and Bette Davis will receive retribution for defying moral codes. Yet of course we know that in real life bad guys score some victories, love affairs can drag on interminably, and the Bette Davis type is that smiling woman next door who has everything we want. And sometimes we wonder what if the ending we saw in the movie was not what really happened."

The Last Desperate Hour

by Robert Thurston

Noodles picked at rust flecks on his .45 automatic. Mrs. Glaze's hands dug through several layers of cellophane wrappings to excavate bread for breakfast. She walked to the toaster. Briskly, as if to get the slices in the slots before the glue hardened.

"Don't turn your back on me, lady." Noodles aimed the .45 at Mrs. Glaze's spine. He winced at the flash of arthritic pain that shot up his arm from his gunhand.

"Of course, Noodles." She turned around. "I forgot again."

"See you remember next time, lady." He lowered the gun. Just in time, because he felt the shakes coming.

"Would you like your coffee now?"

"Yeah. Don't forget to slip a shot o' rotgut in it this time."

"You know what bourbon does to your digestion."

"I like my java served without backtalk, lady."

"Don't blame me when you get sick." Serving the coffee: "Goodness knows what this combination does for your diarrhea."

Junior Glaze hopped into the kitchen.

"Cut the noise, kid," Noodles said, his shaking hand trying to reduce the sloshing of the coffee.

"Hi, Uncle Noodles," Junior Glaze said.

"Hi, Uncle Noodles," gorgeous Veronica Glaze said. She flounced past him, her active hands evening the waistline of her miniskirt. Noodles studied her well-shaped legs. Nostalgia, remembrance of thighs past.

187

"Where's Butch?" he asked Veronica. "He should be down here by now."

"I knocked at his door like always."

"Butch's gotten lazy lately." He flexed his left hand, testing to see if any of the creeping numbness had crept further. "Junior, go get him up."

"Do I got to?"

"Not less'n you don't want your head cracked open by a gunbarrel. Get moving."

"Do what Uncle Noodles says," Mrs. Glaze said.

"He's not my *real* uncle. Are you?"

"If I was related to you, small fry, I'd swallow Drano."

"Junior, go tell Uncle Butch his eggs are almost ready. He's so fussy about cold yolks."

"Okay, but Uncle Butch ain't my uncle either."

Junior charged out the door and collided with his father's legs. Mr. Glaze clipped him playfully on the chin.

"Mother, I'll be out late tonight, maybe all night, so don't wait up this time, huh?" Veronica bit into a raw shredded-wheat biscuit.

"Wait a minute, sister," Noodles said. "Did I hear right or have my ears gone cauliflower? You can't stay out all night."

"Uncle Noodles, this is none of—"

"In my day the only kind of female who stayed out all night was a broad."

"And what do you mean by that little remark?"

"What's up?" Mr. Glaze said, as he entered the kitchen.

"No niece of mine's gonna be a broad."

"Niece of *yours?*"

"I think, dear," Mrs. Glaze said, "that Uncle Noodles means that in his day if a girl stayed out all night it meant she was sexually promiscuous."

"It meant they were—"

"See? Times haven't changed that much," Mr. Glaze said, the tone of his voice sending a bitter message to Veronica, a despairing one to his wife, and none at all to Noodles.

"You *let* her stay out all night?" Noodles shouted. "I don't understand *that!*"

"Permissive upbringing," Mr. Glaze said. Yawning, he mashed his fried eggs with a fork. Noodles, who treated eggs delicately, grimaced.

"I'm glad I got sent up the river when I did. Sophie'd almost got her mitts on me. The old marriage con. Then we'da had kids and I'd be putting up with a dumb broad daughter. Hell, I'd break both her legs the first night she came home in the morning."

"Anyway, Mother, don't wait up." Afterthought: "Let *him*—" nodding toward Noodles—" wait up. He's got to anyway while he's on the night shift."

Noodles grumbled; he couldn't locate the insult in Veronica's remark.

"You just keep your mouth shut with your college-chump friends. Or you know what."

"Uncle Noodles, have I ever squealed on you? You don't have to threaten every time I . . . "

"Can it."

"My dear daring dancing daughter," Mr. Glaze said, sopping up egg yolk with a piece of toast. Noodles looked away, his face white on yellow.

"Looks to me like everyone's got a case of morning jitters," Mrs. Glaze said. "We should all take a deep breath and consider our indiscretions."

"Take a deep, deep, *deep* breath, Veronica," Mr. Glaze said. Shreds of a shredded-wheat biscuit fell from Veronica's tightened fist.

Junior Glaze leaped into the kitchen.

"I knocked and hollered, but Uncle Butch just won't get up."

"Lazy bum," Noodles muttered.

"Eat your breakfast, Junior," Mrs. Glaze said. "I'll go."

"I'll do it," Noodles said. "But don't none of you pull a fast one. I'll drill a hole between the shoulder blades of anybody trying to leave the house or grounds."

He backed through the doorway, his .45 automatic waving from side to side like a rusty metronome.

"Sometimes," Veronica said after Noodles had left, "sometimes I wish he'd just disappear or die or something."

"Die?" Junior said. "You want Uncle Noodles to die!"

"Veronica didn't mean it," Mrs. Glaze said.

"Of course I didn't, but Jesus, it's getting inconvenient. I mean, I can't bring anyone home without Uncle Noodles giving them the onceover."

"We must be patient," Mrs. Glaze said. "Noodles hasn't been out of the house in eighteen years. I think he's afraid of the outside world."

"Poppycock," Mr. Glaze said. He said it so it sounded like an overly masculine flower.

"What?"

"You and your bleeding-heart liberalism, you've always

got to find the compassionate reason for everyone's actions. Particularly Noodles."

Mrs. Glaze began twisting a potholder. Junior pretended to gnaw on a piece of cold toast. Veronica backed slowly toward the door.

"Bleeding heart, eh?" Mrs. Glaze said. "I noticed you were capable of some far-leftist sympathy for oppressed minorities back when they first crashed their way into this house. You could wax pretty maudlin over how a class-bound society drove poor deprived Noodles and Butch into lives of crime. You—"

"I was a political *naif*. A sadsack trying to emulate his misguided labor-organizer father who'd nourished him on all the platitudes of the thirties. A Steinbeckian—"

"Stop sidestepping, you were a regular Commie in those—"

"Bitch! How dare you call me a Communist in front of the children?"

"This is all irrelevant," Veronica said. "Nobody gives a damn about the political sins of the past any more."

"Your mother does, obviously."

"All I want is for my kids to know it was their *father* who, when afforded a *perfect* chance to get the police, decided it was only right that Noodles and Butch get a second chance from the society that—"

"Oh, yeah? I suppose *you* didn't sentimentalize being held captive by escaped convicts. Dear God, I don't know how I make any decisions, what with your sentimentality and Veronica's hardheaded radicalism."

"Father, I was only *three* then."

"What difference does that make? So I didn't turn them in. So sue me." He gave himself thinking time by lighting a cigarette. "Besides, at that time we expected Sophie to show up with the getaway car and money."

"*Aunt* Sophie?" Junior said. "I never saw Aunt Sophie."

"She never showed up," Veronica said.

"Remember, Edith," Mr. Glaze said, "how they'd spring into action at any sound outside the house?"

"Yes, Butch at the window, Noodles hiding in the bushes. They really went at it with energy then. It was grand, it really was."

"See how you sentimentalize," Mr. Glaze said, as he flicked cigarette ash onto a glob of leftover egg yolk.

"You led me into it with your talk of the old days. You—"

"I've got to go," Veronica said at the kitchen door.

Veronica now sat across from him. Her mother had left to serve the refreshments to the mourners. The family had arranged among themselves a schedule in which each of them took regular turns sitting with Noodles during the daylight and evening hours. At night they left him alone by Butch's coffin.

Veronica maintained an obvious silence. As always, she had planted a book in front of her face. He wished everyone would go home so he could move around a little. Shooting pains in his gun arm, numbness in the other, he felt out of balance.

"Would you like anything, Uncle Noodles?" The request was part of her ritual, sometimes the only thing she said on her turn.

"Like for you to gab with me for a change."

"Sure. Name your subject. How about the drug culture? Contemporary British novelists? The naked ape?"

"Don't wisecrack me, young lady."

"All right. But what *do* you want to talk about?"

"Nothin'. Shut up."

Veronica shrugged.

"You was nice to me when we found Butch dead. Why the big change?"

Veronica shrugged.

"When you was a kid, you was always after me to tell you stories. And I told you about my buddies, what they told me in stir. At least the stories you could tell kids. You don't like stories no more, huh?"

Veronica shrugged.

"You like staying out all night with eager studs."

Veronica shrugged.

"Quit shruggin'. Talk to me."

"Not if you're going to treat me like a broad."

"Ah, can it."

Later he talked to Butch for the last time:

"I'm crashin' outta here, Butch. Shoulda left long time ago. Useta be a good hideout. Useta once. I gotta get somewhere where the air's clean. I'll head for the Sierras or somethin'. I'm not scared or nothin', it's not that. These cruds, they're stupid but they can be trusted. But they don't care no more. When'd that start, you notice it? Useta be tension in the air, remember? Remember when it was exciting to come downstairs after a good rest on that soft mattress and go on shift? Hadda be alert them days. No place for a lazy bum. Sorry, Butch. And *they* useta hop and jump when we told 'em to. No telling you what foods to eat, no big-word sarcasm, no talkin' about you in front of your face like you're not there.

"So I'm crashin' out tomorrow. The cruds'll be busy in here with the funeral. And right on the dot at nine o'clock, Red'll come up in the laundry truck. I'll get him to take me. Then we go crashin' outta here on two wheels. He gives me any flap, I plant my .45 in his back and tell him to get the hell going. If I can find out where she stashed the .45.

"Funny, yesterday I was afraid to go out. But you gotta take risks sometimes, ain't that true? Hell, where'd we be if we hadn't taken risks sometimes?

"Don't worry about me, old buddy. I'll make it. I made it this far, didn't I?"

George Alec Effinger—"Piglet"—is represented three times in this volume. I am particularly pleased to have this piece in the book. Gives me a sense of participating in something, a little like the anonymous sailor in Columbus' crew who saw the first land bird. . . .

In the author's own words: "This is the most cherished firstborn. It is a transcript of a nightmare. I woke up shaking, and crawled out of bed to write it. It was about four o'clock, and I was stark naked and freezing, but I couldn't stop the words. My first story: fed up with *society* and stuck in the middle, 'cause bro, the Revolution don't look so cool from here, either. . . ."

"The Westfield Heights
Mall Monster"

Geo. Alec Effinger

> ...*Come the Revolution,*
> *There'll be no more Do-Not-Enters,*
> *No more shopping centers,*
> *Come the Revolution...*
> —Newborn folksong of the
> Street People

It starts like one of the usual monster flicks: they bring the music up, jabbing at you like they think you'll scream at the producer's name. The credits flash in this arthritic alphabet so you know it's going to be *weird;* the names flash off before you can possibly read them. But that's cool, because I really think they're only there for the mood, anyway. So the words go away, and the theme tones down into background Muzak (which you *know* is supposed to set you up for the first horror-hook), and it's completely their move.

You see this street. What's a gas is that it's such a real street. You say, "Wow!" because it ain't a fuckin' desert or top-secret atomic compound. It looks like every Kimberley Drive in every murderous little Anytown, U.S.A. Great place for a monster. It's late at night, mist trapping the light around the streetlamps, no traffic, no people. Some of the houses are still awake, but they're losing consciousness, not one of them watching: welcome to Westfield Heights.

You hear the actors before you get to see them; the camera is dutifully panning past each sad house, underlining so you dig—Home Free. It'd be a little thick if it wasn't so doggone real. After a short while you begin to notice the standard Hollywood walking effects: amplified pebble crunch, shoes scratching the sidewalk as loud as a match striking right by your ear. The houses ease past each other. The swarms of light rain do not hide the tipped tricycle on one lawn, the *Sold!* sign stuck like a knife in one carefully tended other.

You get to the corner. Voices are starting low, idea of distance, laughing, pauses, unintelligible conversation. The camera swings left, down the main street, focusing on a large suburban shopping center. The glistening bare parking lot, the hush and glow, the assured sense of everything-you'll-ever-want gets to you fast: instant identification, no time wasted.

The camera pulls back a bit, dumping the shopping center out of focus. The first car slishes by on the wet pavement. Already a hundred yards gone, the car's headlights pick out two figures in brief silhouette. Zoom in on a Boy and a Girl. Voices up a little.

Even though the boy and girl are on at last, filling the screen top to bottom, their voices aren't up all the way. It still sounds as if they're fifty yards off. I realize we're supposed to be *looking* at them, don't really care what they're saying. I sure don't. After a while I see they're walking to the shopping center: I've got time to get some coke.

Which I do. I dig in my pocket with one hand while I punch the coke-machine button with the other. The packet of coke drops down before I can fumble out my matchbook. (It's cool. Picked it up about a month ago; it's old, a real mind snag: "Do you need $$$? Earn $100-$300 a week in your SPARE TIME!" Be a real estate agent. Wow.)

From the lobby the voices of that chick and the guy are even more smothered. His voice murmurs and growls, like the muffled racket of machines in the distance, hers sounding like drops of water splashing quickly from a great height. The total effect is not bad. I am toying with the idea of staying in the lobby. I am in no hurry to make their acquaintance. And, yes, the movie is judged more dispassionately when not seen and barely heard.

In two quick snorts I dispose of most of the coke, but there's still a lot left in the little cellophane bag. On an impulse I give it to this chick, really sharp, vinyl and metal-stud type. She gives me this sour but bored look: I have come on too strong. I lose. Fucking bitch.

Laughter in shreds, spasmodic titters reach me. I haul ass back to my seat, afraid that I have missed the initial and necessary monstral confrontation. I have not. We are merely digging the lovelies on the screen.

They are effective stereotypes. Like the straited pews of houses, like the Westfield Heights Mall itself, these people are forced into capsular identities, little no-time pills of data that go off with a relay click in your mind.

The chick is small and thin. Her blond hair is cut, as if by a scythe, Whish! wherever it threatens to touch her shoulders. Her face has been chosen with obvious care, its pretty-plainness wavering ambiguously in the uncertain light. Her hands are active, small, glancing off her hair, off her face as constantly as the lightly falling drops of rain. On one hand is a large class ring, its roomy fit made snug by some horrible pink fuzz.

She is wearing an imitation suede skirt with rawhide thongs, a white blouse with pockets designed to accentuate her 32-inch bust (around her neck—the gold-covered heart, inscribed "Paul and Linda"), dirty blue tennis shoes, and a hip-length black imitation-leather coat with trailing belt. She is in the Westfield High A Cappella Choir and the Future Teachers of America. She is a drag, a royal pain, a technical virgin, getting wet but In Love.

This cat Paul is a groove. He's exactly right: the Jock, displaying his very proud blue and white jacket (a shouting Indian embroidered on the back, "Westfield Warriors" sewn around that in a circle). He has very short brown hair, six feet of sturdy frame, and a hulking gait that must be put on. His hands are in the pockets of his jacket, as it seems, permanently. He talks infrequently, preferring to let Linda carry the rest of the evening. He kicks a pebble along the sidewalk for several paces, he nods in answer to her, his expression is sullen, frustrated, resigned, martyred.

Plenty of time to watch them; such pains have been taken that we all know, "Oh, yes. *Them.*" It is ludicrous, we laugh. (I laugh, I feel very nice. The cocaine makes the back of my throat taste metal, it hits me.) It is best not to see flicks like this straight. In the audience we laughing people are making Paul and Linda over in the movie of our minds. I laugh, thinking of what the quiet people are watching, all together as it floods through their eyes. A product vastly inferior, no doubt, unfinished and kept at a rational distance.

From following closely behind, the film cuts to a long shot from within the beadwork of stores, staring out across

the nearly deserted parking lot. Now that the distance between the camera and the actors has multiplied a hundred-
fold, the sound is finally brought all the way up. A very
clever and tricky device.

We listen to Linda, her voice now just a bit raucous as
it stereos out of proportion through the mercury-lamplit
night. They come closer. Is there time, she wonders in front
of J. C. Penney's, is their still time to stop (oh God) at
Carvel's? She must be home soon; at one o'clock she will
be transformed into a grounded teen-age girl. They walk
by the A & P, unaware that the background music has
returned to that ominous mode, unaware that whatever
lurks lurks hard by. Here? In everyone's own Penny Lane
home-away-from-home?

Beneath the blue neon of Bronetti's Paul stifles a yawn.
All the stores are locked-in dark, like the coffee shop with
its red exit-eyes, or half-lit, the suspended and wary in-
somniac guardians. The few cars strewn among the neat
white lines in the lot belong to late bowlers or the patrons
of Westfield Heights Mall Cinema I or II. Great phallic
yellow arrows on the asphalt point out, away, hinting at
the urgency to leave, promising a way out. An equal number accuse, directing their authoritarian notice to us, to
Paul and Linda. At the mouths of their aisles are signs
which sparkle in agreement: *No Exit*.

Like a Greek chorus the music counsels us.

A cut back to Paul, who opens the front door of Carvel's
for Linda. He stands awkwardly, holding it, while she smiles
up at him and brushes by. The night manager comes out
from the back room, called by the door's clarion tinkle.

"Near closing time, kids. You just made it in under the
wire."

Someone says "Oh," and then a pause. The music piles
more strange chords, searching for resolution. The light
inside is very bright, the store is drab with cheerful cutouts
and advertising posters.

"Well, what'll it be?"

"A chocolate shake," says Paul, "with chocolate ice
cream."

"Large or small?"

"Large, I guess."

Linda orders an indeterminate sundae, hovering over the
counter to find a flavor. Paul is reading a sign with feigned
detachment. She is looking alternately at rum raisin and
cherry vanilla.

A very close shot of the back of her head. She glances

up, ready to order. She screams, loud, stridently, so that her voice cracks. The background music is thundering convulsively. The counter man is melting, he becomes a glob, a plastic, shiny, searching mass. Paul yells, pulling Linda away as she cries, pushing her out that fucking tinkly door.

They run the full length of Sears, stopping at last as she coughs, choking with fear and disgust. Paul holds her, not soothing her at all as he stares back in terror. After a few seconds he rouses himself. "Come on," he says, tugging again at her arm, "we better get to the car."

"Paul, God, what *was* it?" she sobs. "What are we going to do?" She hugs close to him, stumbling. The camera watches them hurry away.

There are a few quick touches of laughter in the audience but, if you dig, I think they come from the people who weren't laughing before. I am not laughing. I'm not sure what is happening: a *cinema verité* monster flick?

The film cuts to a position well in front of the couple. A close-up shows Paul urging Linda on, she still crying, shaking her head. Then a slow, deliberate pan to the Record Ranch some yards away. In total silence the front of the darkened store begins to shimmer; the life of the store bubbles through the inanimate construction as it blurs and drips, running together on the sidewalk. Paul and Linda do not notice.

They come upon the oozing corruption suddenly, halting in stunned horror. It gropes, spreading toward them, hissing and gurgling. It probes sightlessly, touching the toe of one of Linda's shoes.

She screams in uncontrolled panic, blinded by her own tears. Paul jerks her to him and throws off her shoe. The mass has swelled, hungrily billowing up, surging in its foulness to crush her down. Paul is shrieking, too, but he hurls Linda free. He supports her, half carrying her toward the car, still so far away.

He pulls her along. She trips on a curb, falling heedlessly. Paul bends to scoop her up. Over her shoulder he sees Korman's Stationery, already a huge boiling puddle of slime. It flows toward her. He grabs her arms as the fuming horror surrounds her foot. It climbs her leg with a sound like the grinding of wet sand. Linda cries out, weirdly subdued, her voice rasping low. Her features are twisted, her face flushed red, her red eyes pleading.

Paul drags her a few inches. He is dazed, and he looks around helplessly. Behind him Wolf & Denny's has formed into a wall-like wave, and he jumps from the sidewalk as it shudders and falls on her, hiding her beneath its slickly rolling surface.

"This movie," I say to myself, "wow!" That dumb chick looked *motivated*. The audience is very quiet. My hands are sweating. "It's a movie," I tell myself. It's only a movie.

The star Warrior, Paul, is running in the street. The music is still down, and the sounds of his weariness are faint. You can hear the cleats on his heels against the pavement, clicking as he runs past the signs telling him to stop.

His car is fifty yards away, twenty-five yards away, ten. His car is glittering diamond points of light, raindrops on the waxed finish. His car is hazy, shifting on the plain of asphalt, its colors running into pools and eddies, its shape no longer defined. It moves, spurred by a secret sense of identity. It writhes; its undulations wink and grin. We are products of our culture, it jokes. It reaches toward Paul to welcome him, too, to the shopping center overmind. The youngster is grown, and may be initiated.

There is silence. The entire area around Paul becomes a restles, starving sea. It is difficult to bring it all together into focus; it mounts into rainbow crests or falls in upon itself, splashing oil-on-water bands of color.

We view from above. In the background, across the grasping sickness that was the Mall, a suburban patrol car cruises. It is sometimes difficult to decide which the cage is protecting from which, and the car passes by.

Paul, surrounded, is struck by a wetly glistening arm of the mass. He falls to his knees and the camera closes on him. A stream of blood runs from his forehead across his nose, his mouth is bloody. It is not Paul's face. The face grimaces, laughing into the camera, and raises one hand in a V (there is some applause from the audience).

Once again Paul rises, screaming silently, fighting, losing, winning in the montage of film clips. He falls, consumed, and is picked up by a heavy uniformed figure. He is shoved against the side of a car and held. Another cop swings a club, backhanded a short way like Vic Power used to with the Indians. He pulls it back over his shoulder, grabs with both hands, and connects.

A voice begins. It is an old recording.

I have nothing to offer but blood, toil, tears, and sweat.

Paul falls once again, and rises, a black man with his head bowed, with a Gold Medal, and a black glove raised on his fist.

The same voice:

...on the beaches, we shall fight on the landing grounds, we shall fight in the fields...

Paul falls, bloody fragments and a strong (but powerless?) heart still beating. He falls again, an old Asian woman, another, bullet-riddled, several young men, children, scores of bodies.

...and in the streets...

A young girl pushes a flower into the barrel of a bayoneted rifle.

A ragged crowd of youths shouts and gestures, and flees the blooming canisters.

The camera moves back, the ravaging monster of Westfield Heights victorious. Already it is settling down, though unsated; perhaps with some sort of alien pride. A pan across the stores reveals the former picture of quiet adequacy, nothing disturbed or disturbing except the "r" in *Sears*, which is thinner than the other letters and flickering.

As the final theme and credits appear, the old, tired, beautiful voice speaks again:

For my own part, looking out upon the future, I do not view the process with any misgivings. I could not stop it if I wished; no one can stop it. Like the Mississippi, it just keeps rolling along. Let it roll on full flood, inexorable, irresistible, benignant, to broader lands and better days.

The house lights come on, the audience is quiet. We are thinking, "This is how it was." The lights go off, signaling the start of the main feature. Although it is something I originally wanted to see very much, I leave my seat. The Selected Short Subject was quite enough. The movies are Free; I will come again.

I make my way up the aisle. I do not think to pause for the Free coke, or any of the other Free machines. I pass through the lobby and outside. I do not glance even at the old ticket window, which always hangs me up (it is sealed now and filled with water and people bring fish to put in it). Westfield Heights is in my ears and in my eyes.

The Terrific Play of Forces
Natural and Human

by Robin Scott Wilson

We are in the midst of a science-fiction boom. Aficionados who once had to search the dark corners of specialty book shops now find their favorite reading material in every supermarket and drugstore newstand. This year, some twenty publishing houses will bring out about 350 science-fiction novels and story collections; another three and a half million words of science fiction will be published serially in the half-dozen or so magazines devoted exclusively to the genre; many other stories will appear in such publications as *Playboy*, *The New Yorker*, *McCall's*, and the lesser men's magazines. Vladimir Nabokov's *Ada* and Kurt Vonnegut's *Slaughterhouse Five* were nominated for the 1969 Nebula award of the Science Fiction Writers of America. Half a hundred colleges and universities now offer courses in science fiction; the prestigious Modern Language Association conducts an annual symposium on the subject and sponsors a scholarly journal of science-fiction criticism; and a prominent textbook publisher is contemplating the issuance of a freshman sourcebook of science fiction, the surest harbinger of academic interest.

But despite all this new interest in science fiction, there remains widespread uncertainty as to just what it is. Is it a distinct, albeit subliterary genre, akin to the detective story and the western? Its primary appearance in pulp magazines might suggest so. Is it part of pop culture, with psychological and social roots similar to those of jazz, the comic strips, and the animated cartoon? Its popularity among the young would seem to imply this. Or can it, despite its frequent irreverence, its tradition of iconoclasm, its excitement and heightened drama, claim the kind of high seriousness—in intent if not in execution—that is traditionally assocated with literature? In other words, is there something in science fiction that warrants the increasing attention it is getting from scholars, teachers, informed readers, and serious literary artists? And if so, what is it? As a reader of science fiction since 1934, a writer of it since 1964, and an academic once engaged in teaching the writing of it, I am convinced there is indeed something there. Just what it is—the unique place science fiction holds in the current state of letters—I hope to discover in the following paragraphs.

First of all, anyone who gives serious critical consideration to science fiction must quickly come to agree with Damon Knight, one of the most sensible critics in the field, that "the term 'science fiction' is a misnomer, that trying to get two enthusiasts to agree on a definition of it leads only to bloody knuckles; that better labels have been devised [e.g., 'speculative fiction'] . . . but that we're stuck with this one; and that it will do us no particular harm if we remember that . . . it means what we point to when we say it."

Bloody knuckles or no, we need a comprehensive definition of science fiction. It is demanded by the increasingly wide public interest in the things students of science fiction point to. And given the growing number of stories containing science-fiction themes and notions, written by persons whose literary reputations extend beyond the once-narrow coteries of science-fiction readers, appearing in publications not usually considered outlets for science fiction, it has become increasingly difficult to know even where to point when we say "science fiction." The time is gone when science fiction—whatever it really is—could be neatly pigeonholed under some such rubric as "imaginative romance," or "pseudo-science," or "science-fantasy," or "utopian fiction." The time for easy categorization is gone and the problem of defining "science fiction" is pertinent precisely because science, its impact on the individual, and its influence on our collective cultural life have all changed so enormously in the past few decades.

There are some serviceable, if not very catholic, definitions of science fiction on the books. They do not display wide variety. Typical is Reginald Bretnor's: science fiction is "that sort of fiction in which the author . . . takes into account . . . the effects and possible future effects on human beings of scientific method and scientific fact." Theodore Sturgeon, one of the grand old men of the business, simply defines science fiction as "a story which could not have happened without its scientific content." And Kingsley Amis, in *New Maps of Hell,* elaborates on Sturgeon a good deal with his statement that science fiction is "that class of prose narrative treating of a situation that could not arise in the world we know, but which is hypothesized on the basis of some innovation in science or technology."

It is difficult to quarrel with any of these statements, but like most substantive definitions, they are leaky vessels whose dripping exceptions can be annoying. Is *Arrowsmith* science fiction? Sturgeon's definition would seem to allow it. How about Book III of *Gulliver's Travels,* the voyage to Laputa? Amis' definition would seem to include it. But neither of these works are what most people usually point to when they say "science fiction." There are some generic exclusions which can be made. For instance, we can exclude that sort of story so prevalent in the late forties—when science fiction rode the shoulders of that apocalyptic fifth horseman, the threat of nuclear destruction, into sudden and unhealthy popularity—in which science and technology provide only background and setting, are artistically nonfunctional. Such are the penny-dreadful "space operas" in which the cowboy's horse becomes a rocketship, his gun a blaster, and his lone prairie the "inky, awesome blackness of interstellar space." To be excluded, too, is the purely satirical utopia such as *Erewhon,* in which—to quote Mark Hillegas—"the author assumes a more ironic attitude toward his subject and is not as consistently serious about achieving verisimilitude, whether scientific or otherwise."

This emphasis on verisimilitude seems to be a consistent element in definitions of science fiction, partly one supposes to distinguish it more clearly from fantasy. But verisimilitude in this context should not be understood to mean the kind of superficial realism which characterizes, say, DeFoe's *Moll Flanders.* Nor should it be applied so as to exclude the interesting experimentation in surrealist stylistic techniques which is so much a part of what Judith Merril and others have called "the New Wave." Verisimilitude in contemporary science fiction is explicated in the phrase "good science fiction is based on good science." But again, a qualification: no one goes to science fiction to learn science; the "good" science of science fiction is good because it does not contravene known science. Thus science fiction, in H. Bruce Franklin's words, "tries to imitate . . . possibilities." It "seeks to describe present reality in terms of a credible hypothetical invention—past, present, or most usually future—extrapolated from that reality." Here the key word is "credible." The verisimilitude of science fiction is posited on the assumption that anything not forbidden is permitted. Hence, such science-fiction conventions as faster-than-light travel by means of "warped space," the hypothesis of "parallel worlds," and the inevitability of confrontation between human and alien can be considered adequately verisimilar because nothing now known to science precludes the possibility that they are true.

Also common to many definitions of science fiction is an insistence that the real business of science fiction is people. For Sturgeon, science fiction is first of all a "story built around human beings, with a human problem, and a human solution . . . " And to Amis' definition, Mark Hillegas makes the "extremely important" addition "that 'quality' science fiction always makes a significant comment on human life . . . "

In summary then, most substantive definitions of science fiction agree that it is a fiction in which science, or some credible extrapolation of science, is integrally combined with an honest consideration of the human condition. Put another way, science fiction juxtaposes the cumulative, empirical, and general knowledge that we call science with the spontaneous, intuitive, subjectively derived perceptions of human reality that have always been the special material of art. And in the nature of this juxtaposition lies the source of much of the dissatisfaction one feels with substantive definitions of science fiction: where does science end and art begin? Isn't man's knowledge of his own condition at least a little bit cumulative? And isn't the way science works a little bit intuitive and spontaneous? To paraphrase Walt Kelly's Pogo, "it's hard to sort jam and marbles."

Perhaps we can supplement these substantive definitions of science fiction by examining more closely what science has come to mean in our time, seeking in that examination a *functional* definition, one which attempts to determine what science fiction ideally does rather than what science fiction is. More specifically, if we consider literature as a varied assortment of subassemblies in the cultural machine, what precise function does the literature of science fiction perform? Or, if we prefer to see literature as something that pleases and instructs, and we take the pleasure of science fiction on content, we may ask how it performs its pedagogic role. The answers to these questions, I believe, lie in the nature of man's relationship to his science.

So explosive has been the growth of scientific knowledge since the late nineteenth century that there has been a qualitative, not just a quantitative, change in its impact on human affairs. The pervasiveness of the influence of contemporary science on mankind would seem to require no documentation. Technological innovation, the legitimate offspring of "pure" science, has transformed our society in almost every particular, and since World War II, applied science has seemed to gaze with Janus-faced ambivalence at the twin futures within its power to achieve: the absolute destruction or salvation of humanity.

One reason for the astonishing growth of science and technology in this century has been, of course, war; but another, and perhaps a more important one, is simply that science has created the conditions—in western society at least—under which it best flourishes: these are affluence, leisure, and a high regard for education. Our society values science very highly; our schools turn out scientists in astonishing numbers. To Professor Purcell of Harvard is attributed the remark that ninety percent of all scientists are now alive. And while the relationship between the accumulation of scientific knowledge and the number of scientific workers is probably not linear, it is proportional.

One result of this explosion of scientific knowledge has been the compartmentalization of scientists from each other and from the lay public, a compartmentalization increased by the production—also inevitable—of specialized language, both literal and mathematical, which further hinders interdisciplinary communications. Paradoxically, while applied science and its material fruits have won for the scientist new status, new acceptance by the public, the increasingly exotic nature of scientific inquiry has made what the scientist does more and more incomprehensible to a public which thanks him for new vaccines, better transportation and communications, and the somato-forming miracles of Lycra fiber. In short, although science has enormous impact on us all, has transformed our society almost beyond the power of words to express, it has steadily made less and less of a contribution to general culture.

One may see the extent of this estrangement between culture and science by comparing the contribution of science to culture in the nineteenth century with its contribution today. One need only recall the public excitement about mesmerism, the innumerable lecture-hall and countyfair demonstrations in which some country Trilby lost a few inhibitions before an enthusiastic audience; or the traveling "professors" who strangled white mice in evacuated bell jars; the bearded scientists who dazzle audiences with the miraculous fireworks of the Tesla coil; the acrimonious public debates between exponents of opposing scientific views; the hours on lecture stages spent by such scientific proselytizers as T. H. Huxley, "Darwin's bulldog." Who now would travel across town to the high school auditorium to hear Professor Murray Gel-Mann describe the fruitless hunting of the quark? Who could understand him if he were to give such a lecture? How could he provide a visually gratifying demonstration of the theory that the cross-sectional probability of quark production is on the order of 10^{-39} square centimeters?

Now this is not to imply that the cultural impact of science in the past was solely a matter of showmanship, although showmanship undoubtedly played a large part in educating the public to support scientific endeavor. (And, of course, it still does. How astonishingly easy it has been to pry $27 billion out of the American public to finance one after another of what the television commentators refer to as "space spectaculars.") What I argue here is that it was the palpable, easily demonstrable quality of scientific discovery a generation or two ago, the strong association of scientific advance with colorful personalities, the narrow gap between applied science and common experience, which enabled science to make a very considerable impact on culture. And conversely, since most scientific endeavor today is the work of large numbers of anonymous team members and has reached a level of abstraction exceedingly difficult to demonstrate to a lay audience—or for that matter to an audience of scientists engaged in other disciplines—the contemporary impact of science on society occurs only at second hand, through the medium of applied technology; and this impact, neither artistic nor intellectual, is not cultural.

Of course, there are exceptions. As J. Robert Oppenheimer pointed out in his remarkable little essay "The Tree of Knowledge," there are newer sciences in which the ideas are "revolutionary but not very hard to understand." Specifically, "in the psychological sciences there are many fundamental points that anyone can understand if he is willing to take the trouble—science here is just beginning to leave the common experience, and the accumulated tradition has not yet grown very far." But it is growing rapidly, one might add, and the communications gap between students of psychology and laymen grows broader with each new discovery in psychochemistry, with the gradual movement away from the individual and idiosyncratic theories of such pioneers as Freud and Jung.

From all this, one can see that modern science poses a peculiar dilemma. On one hand, however remotely, science is a tremendous influence on the quality of all our lives. On the other, it has penetrated ever more deeply into a temple of abstractions whose mysteries are not understandable to very many people. We are being moved by forces we no longer comprehend. Science, which bid fair to "unlock the mysteries of the universe," has itself come to constitute a mystery of very nearly equal obscurity. Technology, the means man has employed to deal with a hostile nature, has itself produced a new environment in many ways far more hostile. Something there is that threatens us grievous bodily harm; that promises us health and longevity; that leads to technologies which poison our air, our water, our mothers' milk; that has virtually eliminated poliomyelitis; that invents cyclamates and then tells us they are carcinogens. We don't understand what it is, and it worries us.

One reaction of mankind to mysterious threat and mysterious beneficence, the bolt of lightning and the unexpectedly good crop, has always been to mythologize. An invariant function of myth, according to Clyde Kluckhohn, is "the gratification (most often in the negative form of anxiety reduction) of a large proportion of the individuals in a society." And it is science (to be sure, through no fault of its disciples) that has made ours the age of anxiety. We would not, perhaps, be so anxious if we knew where it was all leading, to the lightning or to the good crop. But science has no teleology; the "scientific method" and teleology are, by definition, mutually exclusive. And so, consciously or unconsciously, we seek a view of what science has in store for us. We seek myth, a "story telling of origins and destinies." We hope to find in myth a reassurance that the future will hold no surprises we cannot handle; we want an account of the future that will fulfill "the expectancy of the familiar." What a comforting notion is "the expectancy of the familiar" when one contemplates the more frightening aspects of contemporary weapons research! How reassuring it is to accept such mythic statements as "every effective new weapon produces an equally effective defense," or "man will prevail," or—in desperation—*"Gott mit uns."* What I am considering here are the processes of literary extrapolation, of analogy, of prophecy, and these are the processes of science fiction. I advance the thesis that science fiction brings teleology to science, tells of origins and destinies, both asserts and denies "the expectancy of the familiar," is—in brief—both mythopoeic and mythoclastic.

At this point it is worth emphasizing that "myth," a controversial and overworked word in contemporary criticism, is not used in the Aristotelian sense popular in the Enlightenment, as meaning "fable" or "untruth." Allan Watts' definition of myth in *Myth and Ritual in Christianity* is both accurate and comfortably broad: "Myth is to be defined as a complex of stories—some no doubt fact, and some fantasy—which, for various reasons, human beings regard as demonstrations of the inner meaning of the universe and of human life."

What then are the sources of myth? Can myth be consciously created by literary artists, as our functional definition of science fiction demands, or is David Bidney's assertion true that "myth is not something freely invented but a necessary mode of feeling and belief which appears in the course of history and seizes upon human consciousness"?

Here Philip Wheelwright's analysis of myth is helpful. He distinguishes three sorts of myth: "primary myth" (which functions "as a basis, and even perhaps in some instances as a pre-linguistic tendency, of human envisagement"); "consummatory myth" (a "post-romantic attempt to recapture the lost innocence of the primitive mythopoeic attitude"); and "romantic myth" ("as connoting *le roman*, or deliberately contrived story"). It is as romantic myth that I believe science fiction finds its functional definition.

Wheelwright's concept of romantic myth is characterized by his quotation from Richard Chase's *Quest for Myth:* "Myth is literature and must be considered as an aesthetic creation of the human imagination." And Wheelwright continues: "In other words . . . the earliest mythologizers were individual poets—or, by modern analogy, novelists— constructing out of their especially sensitive imaginations tall tales characterized by a peculiar complicaton 'of brilliant excitement, of the terrific play of forces natural and human,' and eventuating in some deeply desired and socially sharable feeling of reconciliation among those forces."

Now this is itself not a bad description of both the substance and the function of science fiction: "tales . . .

characterized by brilliant excitement and the terrific (i.e., 'astounding, exciting awe') play of forces natural and human"; tales which resolve the conflict between natural and human forces in a manner which satisfies a cultural need. Immediately the science-fiction titles begin to come to mind: Asimov's series on robots, surely modern versions of the golem theme; Walter Miller's *A Canticle for Leibowitz*, in which a post-blowup society tries with monkish ignorance to preserve the science which has destroyed it; the prophetic view of post-industrial society and its erosion of human values in Vonnegut's *Player Piano;* the list could be made very long.

I believe many of our best science-fiction writers are fully aware of the mythopoeic function of their art. Lester del Rey, a man of great experience as a writer and editor of science fiction, said at the 1968 Modern Language Association Science Fiction Forum: "Most of sf . . . is nothing in the world but man's need for myths put into written form. We must have myths of one kind or another. Now we have predicting myths, forward-slanting myths. That is the spirit, the soul of sf."

But science fiction is more than a contemporary source of contrived myth, more than a device for mediating between man and the menaces and benefits of a science he has created but no longer understands. While science fiction is indeed mythopoeic, it is also mythoclastic, and it might be argued that the ability of science fiction to provide a running critical gloss on scientific endeavor, to bring opposing values to the unconscious myths of a society fearful of science, being sold on science by its military, governmental, and industrial leaders, is the more important function.

In a sense, our society has been oversold on science. We have come to expect too much of it. If it can deodorize us today, will it not be able to cure our cancers tomorrow? Does not the swift and spectacular progress of science bring substance to the dreams of the perfectabilitarians? If we survive a while longer, if science does not blow us up, can we not hope for a utopia based upon a degree of technological advancement that will once and for all divorce mankind from the exigencies of physical need? Perhaps so. But then what? Will such a brave new world answer to all human aspirations? Can the human spirit thrive in the amnion of a totally benevolent cosmos?

These are the questions which the science-fiction writer poses and attempts, in fiction, to answer. Their answers, the myths he composes, are neither more nor less productive of wisdom than the "answers" of other forms of literature. But whatever the failures and successes of science fiction, in our bifurcated culture, it is the only game in town.

Glen Cook, when he is not affixing the trim to Chevrolet rear windows, writes horrifying fantasy. The economy probably cannot stand another General Motors strike; literature would be improved by it.

This story is a cautionary tale, a view of what can happen here. I hope it is fantasy, but I fear, I fear. . . .

Song from
a Forgotten Hill

by Glen Cook

We were trapped in a world where tomorrow was yesterday. The fire had come three times and gone, and now we were back where our fathers had been a hundred years ago. There were some—"Toms," I've heard them called— who went into slavery as if it were their birthright, but there were also those who fought and died rather than hoe in some redneck's field. Most of those who fought did die. But free.

> "Go tell it on the mountain,
> Over the hill and everywhere;
> Go tell it on the mountain,
> To let my people go. . . . "

The fire came the first time when the good soldier-men in Washington and Moscow decided on mutual suicide. The Russians thought of victory in terms of population destruction. They shot at cities. Our people suffered more than Mr. Charley. We lived in the cities that were the targets. But so did the white liberals who were helping bring change.

The fire came a second time when militants burned the remnants of Whitey's cities. Mr. Charley was too busy with his war to be bothered then, but the fire came a third time when he finished and turned his attention inward. There was civil war between whites and blacks. Might may not make right, but it makes victory. White's Mate.

214

A Fool's Mate. Black loses, and now tomorrow is yesterday.

The war killed most all the good folks. They lived where
the bombs fell. The rednecks and the militants seem to be
the only survivors. And now the rednecks, who waited so
long for their chance, are "puttin' 'em back in their place."
There are very few of us out here in the hills. We're
hunted, and running, but *free*.

My son Al came to me this morning, while I was at the
spring getting water for breakfast coffee. He asked when
we could go home. Said he's getting tired of camping in a
smelly cave. He misses Jamey, the son of the white couple
who lived next door in St. Louis. At five he's too young to
understand a child killed in war. Nor would he understand
if I told him Jamey's father was one of the vigilantes who
drove us south into these hills. He wouldn't understand,
and I'm afraid to try an explanation. Because I don't understand either.

Met a man while I was hunting his morning. Gave me
a rabbit he had extra, for which I was thankful. Said his
name was Duncan X and he was trying to round up men
for a freedom raid into the Bootheel. A lot of our people
working down there, he said. Have to free them. I told
him I'd like to help, but I have a family. Four kids, the
oldest fifteen, and no wife. He looked at me like I was a
monster and traitor, then wandered off through the woods,
carrying his rifle with the safety off. He was wearing old
Army camouflage fatigues. I soon lost sight of him, but I
heard him singing for a long time.

> "Who's that yonder dressed in black?
>   Let my people go,
>   Must be a hypocrite turning back,
>   Let my people go. . . . "

What could I do? I hate the way things are as much as
he, but there are the children to be cared for. I'm sick of
the shooting and burning and dying. We're all Americans.
Aren't we? Why do we have to hate so much? We've got a
nation to rebuild.

After the wanderer left, I went up to my secret place to
pray. It's a lonely, windy place atop a hill burned bald by
an old fire. I usually feel close to God there, but not today.
Lines from a joke I once heard one white man telling another ran through my mind. A Negro was hanging from a
cliff, unable to save himself. He called for God's help and

was told to have faith, to let go, and he would be saved. As he fell, a voice from the sky said, "Ah hates Nigras." I can't help thinking, sometimes, that he hates one of the races. He keeps us fighting on and on. Forever, it seems.

The hunters came while the kids and I were eating lunch. The hounds could be heard while they were still far off. I sent the children down the trail we picked when we first came, then took my rifle and went to see what was happening.

I watched from the underbrush as a dozen men with bloodhounds entered the clearing where I had spoken with Duncan X. They were hunting the organizer, but, from the hounds' behavior, they knew there had been two men in that clearing. They were trying to decide which trail to follow. I sighted on the leader's chest and prayed they wouldn't make me shoot. The Lord must have heard that one. They set off along Duncan's trail. I sighed with relief, but felt more guilty than ever. I hoped he could outrun the pack.

I watched the clearing for a long time after they left, afraid some would turn back to the second trail. Their sort didn't appreciate mine running free. In their own way, they were as afraid as I. Who could blame them? When you treat men the way they do, you have to worry about being hit back. Then everyone's afraid, and fear breeds hate. And hate leads to bloodshed.

I waited, and after a while I followed their trail. They were moving southeast, toward the Bootheel. I turned back after being satisfied of our safety. Trotting, I went after the children. They were waiting quietly in the hiding place we had chosen when we first came into these hills. Little Al thought it a marvelous game of hide and seek, but the others, who were old enough to understand what was happening, were frightened.

"Are they gone?" Lois asked, her brown eyes wide with fright. She was the oldest, and could understand something of our situation. She remembered life before the fire came, and knew the hatreds hatched in the incubator of war.

"They're gone," I sighed. "I want you to say a prayer for Duncan tonight, before you got to bed. He's a fool, but he _is_ one of our people. Come on. Let's go have supper."

As we were nearing the cave, far away, we heard the _pop-pop-pop_ of rifles. I winced. Lois looked at me accusingly. The shooting was in the south. If it was Duncan and his pursuers, then the man was running a circle. "You kids start supper," I said. "I'm going up the mountain for a while." I looked at Lois. She stared back, still silently accusing. I turned and left. There was no point in explaining. She was a militant in her own fashion, and never understood when I did try. As well talk to a stone.

I went up the bald hill, to the little cross I've put there, and prayed. I wondered if God was listening. He'd been terribly unresponsive the past few years. A preacher, just before the war broke, told me the millennium was at hand. I was patiently skeptical at the time, but now it looked as if the man was right. The Lord was unlocking the seven seals and I felt I was living on the Plain of Armageddon. For all I tried putting my trust in God, I felt reservations. He was no longer the loving God of the New Testament. He was the fiery deity who wreaked havoc throughout the Old. Sad.

There were shots again as I came down to the cave. Still far away, but now around to the southwest. Lois had heard them too. When I reached our home-in-exile, she silently offered the rifle. I shook my head. She bit her lip viciously and turned away, saying nothing. The silence hurt more than bitter accusation. We were drifting apart, she and I.

We had a good supper. After a stew made of the rabbit Duncan had given me, I opened a can of peaches and gave the kids a treat. It was usually a holiday when we opened canned goods. Little Al wanted to know which one. Before I could reply, Lois said, "It's the day Judas sold a good man for his own peace."

That hurt, but I didn't pick up the argument. Instead, I took out my old notebook and went outside. As the sun set, I wrote down the day's events, just as I had done since we had come to the cave. After a while, Lois came out to apologize. I said I understood, but I didn't, really, no more than she.

I wrote for an hour, until it was almost too dark to see the paper. The kids came and went, to the spring and back, to the wood pile and back, getting ready for bed and the night. I did not really notice them. I was thinking about Lois, about her growing militancy and her words of accusation. I did not want the kids to sink into the same morass of hatred which had already claimed so many. Neither did I want them to think me a "Tom." I did not think myself a "Tom," but Duncan X, and those who believed as he did, said those who went into slavery also denied it. I began to feel a great sadness. Was there no reasonable alternative to hatred and fighting? There was slavery, of course, but that was not an alternative. It must all be a cosmic jest, or a chess game. Would the Ivory and Ebony play to the last piece? Would God, or the gods, then declare a draw? Sad.

In my preoccupation, I did not see the running man coming up the hill. He was almost on me before I noticed him. A fall of loose rock warned me when he was about twenty feet away. I jumped up and started to go after the rifle. Then I recognized him. Duncan X. Panting, staggering, his clothing torn, blood oozing from a dozen gashes. His pack was gone, and his canteen belt, but he still carried the rifle. I waited till he came close.

"Mon, you gotta hep me," he said. The fear in his voice was the same I had heard before the kids and I left the mess in St. Louis. "Mon, they gon' kill me!"

"What happened?"

"Dogs . . . dogs caught me. Killed 'em, all but one. Mon, they chewed me bad."

"Come inside. We've got a first-aid kit. Lois!"

She came out, looked at Duncan's wounds, and threw her hands to her cheeks.

"Clean up those gashes," I said. "Bandage him if we've got anything."

"Mon, they gon' kill me!" The loud, confident rebel of the morning was gone. He was a hundred and twenty years of scared nigger, running from a lynch mob. When the ropes came out, and the hounds and the guns, he was every black man who had ever run from redneck "justice." He was afraid, and running, probably a dead man, and didn't know why.

"Go ahead. Fix him up," I told Lois. "Heat up some of that stew."

She looked at me strangely, questioningly, making no move. I took the rifle from Duncan's hands, though he tried to stop me. He clung to that weapon like a drowning man to a log. It was the only salvation he knew. It was the only salvation anyone seemed to know these days. Lois watched me take the gun, then took Duncan's hand and led him into the cave. I watched her go, wondering what it was like to be an adult at fifteen.

As the moon came up, I walked back the way Duncan had come. I heard the hound baying, not more than a mile away. Hard. I didn't like things this way, but my decision had been made for me.

I chose my position carefully, behind a large log at the edge of a clearing. They were not long in coming.

The hunters had chosen to leash their remaining hound, keeping him where he could be protected. And there were only nine men. If Duncan had gotten the other three, they wanted him worse than ever. They might not quit till they were all dead, or had their "buck" swinging from a tree. I knew sadness again.

I put the first shot between the hound's eyes. He yelped once, leaping toward the moon. I emptied the clip among running men, but hit no one. They reacted quickly. Rifles and shotguns boomed, peppering the woods around me. I ran, trying to keep low. Without that hound they would have a hard time following.

The shooting stopped a moment later. They realized they were wasting ammunition, trying to murder an empty forest.

I returned to the cave. Lois had fed Duncan, and patched him, and had put him in my bed. He was sleeping, though fitfully, like a man with bad dreams.

"What'd you do?" she asked, at once frightened of and for me.

"Shot their dog. They won't be tracking Duncan or me without him."

"Oh."

"Stoke up the fire a little, will you? I want to do some writing while I'm watching. Then get to bed. It's been a bad day."

"But Duncan . . ."

"I'll look after him. You just go on to bed."

She went. I wrote for a while, then leaned back to think. Eventually, I dozed off. A couple hours must have passed.

I started awake. There were sounds outside the cave. The fire had died to coals. Carefully, I reached for the water pitcher and used it to drown the remains. A figure moved across the cave mouth, outlined by the moonlight. White man! His skin shone in the light. I took the rifle from the table and fell into a prone position. I waited while they talked it over out there. They seemed certain their quarry was inside. I didn't know how they had found the cave—blind luck, probably—but once here, they knew they had their man. I remembered having seen Duncan's fatigue jacket outside, a dead giveaway. I cursed myself for being fool enough to expect them to stop after losing their hound.

They didn't bother with a warning or to-do about surrender. They came in the cave, trying to sneak up on

Duncan. I started shooting. The .30-.06 roared like a cannon in the confinement of the cave. The muzzle flashes splashed white faces with orange light.

I never was much good at killing, not in Vietnam, not here. They were less than twenty feet away, but I only hit one, in the arm. They got out before I could get another.

The shooting woke the kids. Lois slipped up beside me where I lay in the cave mouth, asking what had happened.

"Never mind!" I snapped. "You get the kids out the hole in back. Go up to the hiding place. I'll meet you later."

"Aren't you coming?"

"Lois, neither Duncan nor I can get through that passage. It's too tight. Now get."

As if to punctuate my argument, the rednecks opened up. It was like a regular war, like I saw in Vietnam. They were all over the slope. Bullets whined and pinged as they bounced from one cave wall to another. Lois left, dragging the younger kids down the small tunnel which opened on the far side of the hill.

Duncan crawled up beside me. "Right side fo' me," he said. "How many?"

"Eight. Nine if you count the one I wounded. Didn't think they'd find us after I shot their dog."

"Mon, them honkies half dog themselves. One day you gon' learn."

We shot at muzzle flashes. Funny. Of all the stuff I had in the cave, ammunition was the one thing not in short supply. And me a peaceful man.

"Hey, Duncan," someone downslope shouted, "who's that up there with you?"

"Who's that?" I asked, whispering.

"Jake Kinslow. Him an' me met befo'."

"Hey, Duncan boy," Kinslow shouted, "you better come out before you get your friend in trouble. Whoever you are, mister, this ain't none of your nevermind. We got no argument with you. We just want that rabble-rousing, baby-raping nigger in there with you."

I looked at Duncan. His teeth gleamed as he grinned. "I shacked with his daughter befo' the war. He gon' get even now."

To hide my reaction, I turned and snapped a shot in the direction of Jake's voice. There was a cry. I was surprised.

"Jake, I'm hit!" someone screamed. "God, my leg, my leg!"

Laughing, Duncan reached over and punched my shoulder. "Seven," he said.

"Mister," Jake shouted, "we're gonna hang that nigger. You don't get out, we might hang you too. We got no cause to be after you yet."

Yet. Meaning they were going to be if I didn't get out of their way. But how could I, even if I wanted to? They had put me in a position where I had no choice.

Time passed. We exchanged shots, but the firing dropped off. The moon eventually rose to where it was shining directly into the cave. I glanced at my watch, miraculously still working. Eleven. It had been a long, strange day, and still wasn't over.

A scream downslope drew my attention. I recognized it. Lois!

They dragged her into the moonlight, where I could see her. Jake shouted, "You up there! You see what we've caught hanging around, spying? Know what we're gonna do? Same thing Duncan did to *my* daughter, unless you come out."

I growled deep in my throat. "Let her go!" I shouted. I rose and started out, but Duncan tripped me and dragged me back.

"We'll let her go when we get Duncan!" Kinslow shouted. "Meanwhile, we're gonna have some fun."

I tried to get a clear shot at the man holding Lois, but he stayed behind her, no matter how much she struggled. Duncan dragged me back again. "They're going to rape her!" I snarled. "Let me go!"

"Mon," he said, grinning wickedly, "they gon' rape her anyway. They's honkies. Gon' kill us an' rape her anyway."

"No!" I suddenly shouted, coming to a sudden decision. He had an expression of surprise on his face when I hit him with the gunbarrel. It faded as he fell. "You!" I shouted down the hill. "Jake! Let the girl go! I'll throw Duncan out to you!"

"No! Don't do it!" Lois screamed. "They'll kill you anyway!"

"Throw him out first!" Kinslow yelled.

"Let her go!"

"Tell you what. We'll bring her up and trade you."

I thought for a moment. "All right. But just one man."

They were quiet for a while. Lois kept screaming for me to stop, till they gagged her, but I couldn't throw my daughter to them to save someone like Duncan. "All right, mister," Jake called, "I'm coming up. You bring that nigger out. No tricks. Pretty girl gets it if there are."

I saw movement below, near the edge of the trees. Lois, being dragged by a white man. She was kicking and scratching, but he ignored her. They came up the hill. When I judged they were close enough, I lifted Duncan and went out. He was half-conscious, just enough to stand with my help, not enough to understand what was happening.

Jake stopped about five feet away. He held a pistol to the side of Lois' head. He grinned. "Okay, boy. We trade."

"Let her go."

He moved slightly behind my daughter. He grinned again. "Dumb nigger!" he whispered, then dove behind rocks toward which he had been moving.

The rifles barked all around the cave. I felt bullets hit Duncan. One caught me in the thigh, spinning me away, back into the cavern. As I fell, I saw Lois stagger and try for the cave, but Kinslow fired around the rock.

"Only one of you in there now, black boy," he laughed. "And we're gonna get you. Gonna have a real old-fashioned hanging."

I suppose they are. That was twenty minutes ago. I'm writing this by moonlight, as they creep closer. The bullets are coming in a steady rain, ricocheting throughout the cavern. One will get me any minute. The King of Ivory wins another match. Sad.

I forgot. All the good ones were dead. I trusted bad ones. If God is in a better mood later, I guess I'll have all eternity to think about it. Hatred. It's sad.

> "Go tell it on the mountain,
>   Over the hill and everywhere;
>   Go tell it on the mountain,
>   To let my people go—"

Maggie Nadler is an engineer in St. Louis. In this poignant story, she examines some consequences of one obvious solution to the population problem. Her comment: "I've been asked why I chose the present tense for "The Secret." Present tense conveys a special sense of immediacy, urgency. Thus it seemed only natural to use it in this story of people caught up in a web of ever-nearing horror which they are powerless to alter or escape. . . ."

The Secret

by Maggie Nadler

Sixteen-year-old Sally Morgan nods in response to her mother's words. She will not go to school today; tomorrow she will bring a note stating that she was sick. She knows what this means: her mother has been asked to take over the day shift again temporarily and she, Sally, will be needed at home during those crucial hours between nine and five. She brushes a stray lock of brown hair back from her forehead and tries to concentrate on her breakfast, although she is not hungry. It doesn't work. She pushes away the toast and eggs in disgust. Her stomach is churning. The fear is always there. Her eyes meet her mother's, remain locked for a moment in perfect understanding, and drop to the table again. On a nearby shelf, the radio is blaring away—a noisy early-morning news program. She turns it up a bit louder. The baby may wake up at any minute and start crying. Better to risk the anger of that old biddy in the next apartment than to let the sound of crying get out. It is always this way. Her fair, pretty face, sobered with the weight of early responsibility, breaks into a frown.

Across from her, her younger sister Jill is dawdling over her breakfast as usual, picking at it bite by dainty bite, studying it, worrying at it. She will finish it all, eventually; she always does. But why won't she hurry? Her fastidiousness, accompanied by that exasperating sullenness, annoys Sally, although she tries hard to be patient.

At the stove, their mother is preparing the baby's formula. Sally's mind returns to the problem at hand, the same problem always at hand: the baby. A little modern-day Moses swaddled in blankets instead of bulrushes. It would all be rather pleasantly exciting if it were not so terrifying. The little baby brother, blond, beautiful, ten months old, in constant danger . . . how she loves him! So here she will be today, stuck in the tiny three-room apartment, the dingy, cramped apartment with walls like pasteboard, when she could be at school with her friends. She sighs. David has been attentive lately; she's almost certain he really likes her. Now she won't see him for a whole day, maybe longer. But she is needed here. She turns her attention back to her sister; as soon as Jill has finished eating, Sally will clear the table and do the dishes. Why won't the kid hurry?

Sitting stubbornly hunched over her breakfast, picking at it, slowly but surely making it disappear, thirteen-year-old Jill—thin-faced, sullen—glowers up at her sister. Darn Sally anyway, putting on airs, acting just like a grownup, and all on account of the brat. She used to be fun, but not any more. Now, do this, do that, yak, yak, yak. And why? We had to be different, have one more baby than everybody else. Privileged character. Mom says it's because of Daddy just dying and all, she wanted his last baby, but I know different. She wanted a *son*. Yeah. Sally and me were always a big disappointment to her even if Sally's too dumb to see it. *Take good care of your brother, now.* Brother, brother, brother this, brother that. Big deal. Just a stupid baby, and we have to have a big fuss. Nobody visits us; I can't even have my friends over. Darn Mom and Sally. I hope somebody finds out. . . .

Jill has finished her breakfast now, flings down her napkin defiantly, and gets up. As she does so, Sally catches a look on her face that she has never seen before. Or rather, has seen many times but failed to interpret correctly. *My God! She hates the baby!* Just like that: suddenly she knows. The thought is hideous. *God! What if—no, that couldn't ever happen—but then again, what if—* Slowly, her mind in a turmoil, she begins to clear away.

And then there is the mother, moving about the kitchen with an energy which masks the quiet desperation of the doomed or nearly doomed. Days like this one are the worst. She cannot bear to be away from home during the daylight hours. If only she could call in sick, but she doesn't dare. At forty, she is partially handicapped; arthritis has worked its calciumed way into the fine joints of her

fingers, making excessive hand motion an agony, dis-
qualifying her for most kinds of work. With jobs so scarce,
she must hang on to the one she has, and therefore her
work record must be perfect in all respects. She is fortunate to have a job at all. The one she holds now—radio
dispatcher for a taxi company—was obtained for her
through the influence of the foreman at Richard's plant,
out of pity or perhaps even a sense of guilt. Richard.
Richard. Richard, unable even to get insurance on account
of the heart condition. But it wasn't his heart that killed
him, finally, but a great chunk of metallic debris, loosed
prematurely by an incautious crane operator, striking him,
crushing him out of all semblance to humanity. Richard.
Richie. Dick. Dickie. Rick. The name in all its variations
and inflections rolls around in her mind for a while like
pinballs in a machine. The names are charged with emotion: father and son coalesced. Richard, the father, her
husband, and Dickie, his son.

Suddenly she stiffens. What is that scraping noise beyond
the thin wall? Miss Hadley on the other side, moving her
chair a bit closer, the better to hear you, my dears? She
often does that. So far she hasn't heard much of interest;
from long habit, her next-apartment neighbors keep their
voices down when in the kitchen. But that doesn't stop her
from trying. In all the years they've lived next to her,
they have never been in her apartment nor she in theirs,
yet they know her well enough from seeing her around
the building, from the pounding on the walls and the
querulous voise raised in protest against the noise they
make. Malicious old bitch, always spying on the neighbors
in as many ways as she can dream up. She has had a
one-way glass panel installed in her door and often sits
behind it keeping an eye out to see who calls on blond
Miss Coombs across the hall, plus whatever other interesting tidbits of information she can manage to pick up. Once
she was even observed, binoculars in hand, peering into
a window of a building across the way. And so on. At
least she hasn't complained about the radio yet today.
With luck, maybe she won't at all.

Miss Hadley would dearly love to cause trouble for her
neighbors, but she's stalemated there; they have an advantage which may press at any moment. Cats. Miss
Hadley has cats: four of them, two more than the zoning
rules permit. The Morgans know this because they have
often seen the animals make the perilous leap from Miss
Hadley's window sill to their own and back again. She

knows that they know. However much she may hate everything else in the world, she loves those cats. And so, the
uneasy truce: don't bother us and we won't report you.

The mother stands very still, listening intently, but there
is no further sound. Perhaps she has only imagined it.
She has become hypersensitive (and why not?) and her
mind sometimes plays tricks on her. She feels ill now, and
very tired. If only Rchard were still here. He would know
what to do. Richard. Richard. Richard—

"Mother! What's wrong?" It is Sally's voice, from far
away.

She realizes that she has been standing rigid, trembling,
with her teeth tightly clenched against a scream.

Miss Priscilla Hadley, gaunt, white-haired, and prim,
never loved by man or cherished by family, sits alone in
her apartment. She is not listening through the walls now,
nor is she observing the world from any one of her custo-
mary vantage points. She scarcely notices the radio blast-
ing away next door. She is weeping. Great sobs wrack her
as she twists on the sofa-bed. Her beloved cats have been
poisoned. One of them, old Tom, companion of a dozen
years, has just died; another, Scruffy, is in great pain and
is obviously not going to live. The other two will probably
recover. For a long time she remains on the bed, her head
buried in her hands. If she ever catches up with whoever
did this . . . It has to have been deliberate. Somebody fed
them something. *Please let me find out who it was.* But she
knows it's hopeless. The world is full of dirty, vicious cat
haters. It could have been anybody.

After a while she gets up and goes to the phone to call
the Animal Protective Society. She will have Scruffy put
to sleep and both cats cremated; she cannot bear to think
of them ending on a trash heap. While dialing, she first
becomes aware of the noise. It's that family on the right
again, the woman and those two teen-agers. Once she had
hoped for children of her own; now the very thought ap-
palls her. She wonders which of the three is responsible for
the constant racket: all of them, probably, acting in perfect
accord. It would be just like them; tight-mouthed, antisocial
bunch, won't give you the time of day but, when it comes
to annoyances . . . At this moment, her thoughts are
interrupted by the sound of a voice at the other end.
She makes the arrangements. A man will come to pick up
Scruffy and Tom; the ashes will be returned to her later
in the week. As she hangs up, she is aware of the sound

of a nearby door slamming; mechanically, she goes over to her own door and looks out. Yes, it's them; that mousy nobody and the younger girl. Strange, the mother doesn't usually go out mornings. Despite her distracting grief, impressions click in her mind with computer like precision. And where's the older one? Brats, both of them. Her lip curls slightly in disgust as tears well up in her eyes again. They had better not annoy her today.

The baby awakens and begins to wail fretfully. Sally hurries to give him his bottle. Jill and mother, barely on time, leave the apartment together. Downstairs, on the sidewalk, they separate. Jill walks in one direction, toward school, her mother in another, toward the monorail stop.

Mrs. Morgan boards the mono at the station. Her arthritic hand fumbles with the token while the conductor looks on in irritation and people jostle behind her. She gets it in the slot, finally, and moves forward. She is lucky; there is one seat left in the rapidly filling car. She sinks into it gratefully. At first she tries to distract herself by reading the advertisements posted in neat rows above her head. But the signs—BUY LIFE INSURANCE . . . SUPPORT OUR BOYS IN BOLIVIA . . . FIGHT CRIME: REPORT INFRACTIONS—are disquieting and eventually she turns her attention inward while allowing her gaze to wander. At once her thoughts crowd tumultuously in upon each other, filling her head, pounding out against the optic nerve in a steady, relentless rhythm: Baby. Danger. Please God. Baby. Danger. Please God. Baby. Danger. Please . . . She is so alone, so frighteningly alone in the world. If only there were some relatives or close trustworthy friends to take in one of the children! Something might be worked out. But there is no one. How long can luck hold out? Surely there are other women, perhaps many, perhaps nearby, doing the same thing she is doing, but she will never know who they are, or how numerous, or how they manage. Yet they must exist, each one living her own personal twenty-four-hour nightmare, a far-flung secret sisterhood united in guilt and terror. It is necessary for her to believe in their existence; otherwise, she would not be able to go on. Her mind grasps frantically at straws of reassurance. There have been many cases—haven't there?—of people hidden successfully for long periods of time, for years, even. Slaves, during the Civil War (she remembers this from fifth-grade history). Or even (dimly recalling another textbook) during World War II in Europe, enemies of the—what were they called—Nazis? Of course it's possible. She's read it. It will only be for two years more. Sally finishes school then, and pretty as she is, she'll have no trouble finding a husband right away. *And after that we can move somewhere else and pass ourselves off as a two-child family. Jill will be old enough to take on more responsibility by then, not that she'll be able to replace Sally, of course, but at least we'll be safe.*

Moving. The thought presents new worries. With housing so scarce, it may take a while. But she will not allow herself to think about that so far in advance. They'll find something when the time comes. For the time being, they are very fortunate to live in a building where, with the exception of the inquisitive Miss Hadley, people mind their own business. Only Miss Hadley takes an interest in their doings, and with care, she can be circumvented. It could be worse, much worse. Thank God Dickie is a relatively quiet baby. His occasional crying can easily be covered up by the sound of the radio. If he were the type to cry all night, it would have been hopeless. *But we've survived for ten months; the worst is past.* Of course, it's a lonely life. No one has visited the apartment in well over a year. It must be awfully hard on the girls not to be able to have their school friends over.

The car lurches suddenly at a sharp curve and a stab of searing pain shoots through her abdomen, souvenir of that night ten months ago when, with only Sally to assist her, she gave birth, twisting on the rock-hard mattress of Jill's bed and muffling her screams in a pillow. Tears well up in her eyes and she turns her head to stare out the window. It's an unfortunate moment to choose. To her right, only feet away, the massive white hulk of the Public Abortion Clinic sails by. PAC, focus of all her troubles and guilts. Only two children to a mother, in this society. But you want more? Sorry, madam. That's the law.

And she has dared to defy the law, she, a gray-haired, poorly educated, careworn widow of forty, one woman alone against the world. When she felt the forbidden life within her, she did not destroy it but rejoiced, and she wore loose clothes and thanked God that she was large-boned and Dickie a small baby who scarcely showed. Now she must deal with the consequences.

Suddenly she snaps out of her reverie. It's her stop, and she nearly missed it. She jumps up and gets off just in time. This is fortunate. The stops are far apart, and had she ridden to the next one, she would have had to walk a long way and would undoubtedly have been late. She hurries across the platform and down the stairs past the three lower tiers of monorail tracks. She wishes they had a phone so she could call Sally around noon to check up on the baby.

Sally has fed the baby and crooned to him and rocked him to sleep in her arms. Now she carries him back to his "bed"—an old hamper lodged deep within the recess of the large bedroom closet, hidden from view by hanging clothes. What a place for a kid . . . but it has to be, she reminds herself. As she tucks him in, her attention is attracted by a slight rustling noise in one corner. Kneeling, she peers into the gloom, and sees a small hole where the wall meets the floor. Oh, no! Mice? Or rats? Surely not rats. Mice, more likely. The building in which they live is theoretically not a tenement, just as their neighborhood is theoretically not a slum, but they've had trouble with rodents before, although not recently. Sally does not like rodents; she has heard that they sometimes attack sleeping children. What should she do? She heads for the kitchen, hastily searches the cabinet above the sink. Yes, there it is: the nearly empty box of rat poison left over from some long-forgotten time. Hastening back to the closet, she sprinkles blue crystals liberally around the hole. There. That's better. The box is now empty. She throws it in the trash bag, which she notes is almost filled. She may as well empty it now. There is nobody in the hall. Little Dickie is safely asleep. Violating her mother's rule that he must never be left alone, even for an instant, she slips out, for just one moment, to the trash closet.

Miss Hadley sits in her kitchen eating the one sausage a day she permits herself. The sausage is long and plump, liberally sprinkled with sauerkraut and sheathed in a stiff bun; Miss Hadley chews it with the brisk short jawstrokes of one to whom ingestion is a distasteful chore to be completed as quickly as possible. Since she eats only to keep up her strength, she is taking her noonday meal today exactly as usual. After finishing, as usual, she disposes of all her garbage (wrapping paper and a few crumbs) in the trash closet down the hall.

Miss Hadley enjoys going through other people's trash and garbage: it is one of her dearest pleasures. In addition to obtaining valuable insights into her neighbors' lives, she occasionally finds some very good scraps for her cats. Now she spots a new waste bag that hadn't been there the day before and, from force of habit, examines it avidly. Her hawk-eyes are drawn at once to a small cardboard container, a cylindrical box with a bright red label bearing a skull and crossbones: DANGER.

Danger.

Danger. Poison. The cats. Immediately, everything falls into place. The blood drains from her face; her hands tremble. Feverishly she flings herself upon the pile, digging, tearing, clawing, through apple cores and orange rinds and potato peels and used tissue, all the way to the bottom, where she finds some papers. One of them is a crumpled envelope. She smooths it out and reads the name of the addressee: Mrs. Mildred Morgan. Morgan! It's them! Of course, who else, dirty scum, filthy rotten swine! They have the apartment next to the fire-escape platform. It would have been easy for them to put something out there. The fact that the Morgans have never shown the slightest animosity toward her pets is disregarded in the voluptuous wave of fury that possesses her. She sways, wringing her hands. She'll get them for this. She'll get them, she'll get them, she'll get them.

But how? A feeling of helplessness overtakes her. She won't be able to prove anything against them. The most she can do is complain to the landlord about their radio and maybe he will force them to keep it down. And that's not enough, oh, no, not nearly enough. No punishment is really great enough for them. But she'll think of something. She'll think of something if it takes the rest of her life.

Tears of rage and grief well up in her eyes and her whole body begins to tremble violently.

Jill gets home at four o'clock. She is in a vile mood, sulky and defiant. One of her friends has just asked her, for the nth time, why they can't play at *her* house for a change. She is sick of the story of an alcoholic mother who prevents her from bringing friends home. As her friends have pointed out often enough, Roz's mother is alcoholic and Roz has people over all the time. It's nothing to be ashamed of. So Jill has to say that her own mother is not only alcoholic, but violent. She stomps into the bedroom, flings herself down on her bed, and immerses herself in a teen-love comic book. Oh, she's so tired of it all.

Mrs. Morgan is home by five-thirty, weary but full of questions about Sally's day. She doesn't have to fix supper;

Sally has already prepared it, as a surprise. The three of
them sit down to casserole and canned soup. The radio is
going. Sally and Jill exchange sharp words across the table;
their mother referees tiredly. Jill is whining now about
how she never has any fun and how she wishes they didn't
have to live this way. The mother's abstracted replies show
that she is only half listening. She doesn't suspect, Sally
thinks, she really doesn't notice. Maybe it's better that
way—or is it? But nothing will happen. Everything will be
all right.

At six, the sky suddenly darkens. There's going to be
a storm. Yes, there it is, the first crashing peal of thunder.
Mrs. Morgan rushes to Dickie's bed. He is awake, and
frightened. He can hear the thunder and he is afraid of
storms. He's going to start crying any second. She carries
him into the living room. Sally quickly turns the radio
louder, then goes to sit beside her mother on the couch.
Jill takes a chair. The four sit locked in a private world of
sound: heavy rain-patter punctuated by bursts of thunder,
baby's crying, and above it all, the sensual pounding of
the radio music. Thump. Thump. Thump. Thump, goes
the heavy beat. Rain. Thunder. Baby. Music. Rain.
Thunder. Baby. Music. Rain. Thunder. Baby—
  Baby.
  The music has stopped.
  The radio has gone dead. The lights are out.
  And suddenly the shrill, plaintive wailing of the baby
can be clearly heard against the counterpoint of storm
sounds. Quickly, Mrs. Morgan claps a hand over Dickie's
mouth, causing him to sputter and gasp. For a timeless
moment she holds it there and then, mercifully, the music
starts up again. Huddled together, she and Sally exchange
frightened whispers. Has anyone heard? Noticed? No, of
course not. It was only for a second. Nobody would notice,
not even that old bat next door, unless she happened to
be listening for it right at that particular instant. We've
got to stop being so paranoid. Other people aren't keeping
track of every single move we make.

Seated in a hard-backed chair in her tiny antiseptic
kitchen, Miss Hadley presses her ear against the wall. She
has been in this position for hours, ever since the younger
daughter got home. She is waiting for them to say something about her cats. They will, eventually. She knows they
will. Miss Hadley's ears are sharp, but not sharp enough
to hear over the din of the radio. Still she perseveres,

fascinated, obsessed. The guilty always reveal themselves. She will catch them eventually. A storm has come up, but she hardly notices, even when cold rain blows in her open window. All her attention is riveted upon that one tiny fragment of space, that microcosm where her ear meets the wall. Her head is filled with infernal music, throbbing, pounding. . . .

Then suddenly, without warning, the lights go and the music dies out, giving way to another sound. It's only for an instant, but in that instant she knows. A shrill sound. A wailing sound.

Of course! Casual observations, snips of information collected over the past months and mentally filed away for future reference now click with deadly accuracy in her computer-mind. So that's what they've been up to all this time! A baby; how very perfect! She'd had babies too. Her cats were her babies, and now they're gone. The images of Tom and Scruffy float lazily in the black void behind her eyeballs as, shaking with excitement, she reaches for the telephone.

The mother sits sobbing wildly, face buried in her hands, flanked by those two scared-looking daughters of hers, while the policeman talks to her in a gentle but firm voice. Why did she do it? She knows the provisions of the law. No, he's not allowed to divulge who reported them. And so on. He feels sorry for them all: when will people learn?

He and his discreetly invisible plainclothes partner turn to go. The woman flings herself upon them, kicking, scratching, biting, screaming. They are prepared for that. The officer pulls an inhaler-sedative cartridge from his pocket and clamps it over her nose and mouth while his partner holds her. Within seconds she is unconscious. Before leaving, the cop feels called upon to administer some words of comfort, which he addresses to the older girl.

The infant won't suffer, he assures her. It's entirely painless. He'll just be sleeping and he'll never wake up. That's all there is to it. Now it is her turn to burst into hysterical sobbing. White-faced, the younger one approaches her sister and awkwardly tries to put her arms around her. The older girl jerks away. She screams a profanity. She slaps the younger girl again and again, with all her strength. The child stumbles backward into a corner and cowers there in terrified incomprehension. The officers wonder what it is all about: just hysteria, probably.

The two turn to leave once more. The uniformed one goes back into the bedroom and gently picks up the sleeping baby. Absently, he runs a hand through the downy hair. He loves children but he also knows about the evils of overpopulation. He has been to the Police Academy. He is a good citizen. He has two small boys of his own and his wife has been sterilized. He displays the flag on Flag Day.

Tenderly bearing their sleeping burden, the two men leave the apartment behind them and disappear into the night.

Joe Wehrle, Jr., is a commercial artist and illustrator who lives in Punxsutawney, Pennsylvania, the home of the Punxsutawney groundhog, whose annual meteorological predictions are heeded across the country. Perhaps that is why Joe writes so understandingly of small, fey creatures like the bandemar. He writes: "This is one of the tales of the Narbek Forest which got their start in a 'Fanzine' comic strip six years ago. Since that time I've learned a lot about the Narbekians and their environment through a series of stories and, currently, a novel. I hope the pipeline to Narbek stays open. . . ."

The Bandemar

by Joe Wehrle, Jr.

The lightning flashed intermittently, piercing the darkness that cloaked the thick Narbek Forest. The wind drove bold curtains of leaves across the tangled paths, warning of the deluge to come.

Fawn the Dark-Eyed ran, clutching the sack of kluroot to her, strong wind pressing the brief skirt against her thighs. The girl was still a long distance from the tree-community, but there was no hope of reaching it now; the only safety—and the only protection for her precious burden—lay in finding a quick refuge here. The distance from Owlstree to her own community was an uncrossable one when it meant transporting dry kluroot through a storm.

This particular garnering was desperately needed, for the wandering sickness approached, and the scarce contents of her sack, kept dry, represented immunity for everyone in the tree-carved dwellings. If the root, once dry, became saturated except under the right conditions, a destroying mold almost always set in. Fawn wrapped the bag in her cloak as a temporary protection.

The rain fell heavily and the wind continued to rise. Fawn searched ever more anxiously, ignoring the fact that she was losing track of her direction.

It was increasingly difficult to see, due to the storm's fury, so she nearly ran past the hollow thafa trunk. It was huge and the opening was away from the wind's direction. Fawn stumbled inside, throwing herself down against the inner wall gratefully.

There the girl remained, contentedly enough, watching

the violence outside. She had removed her outer clothing, using her small, jeweled ear ornaments to tack them to the fibrous wall above her. The kluroot sack reposed safely in a small cleft in the inner wall.

From time to time the wind changed direction, blowing a little rain and a few leaves into the hollow trunk, but not disturbing her much.

On one of these occasions, a very large, dried seed pod came sailing in. Fawn noticed with some surprise that a thin vine was looped through the top, as if the pod had been tied to a branch. She leaned forward to study it.

A small form squeezed out the torn side of the pod with no warning, alarming the girl a little. It was light-green and stood on two spindly legs. The creature had a round head, distinguished most by its one gleaming transparent orange eye. The closed, sunken lid on the other side suggested that some misfortune had befallen its other eye. A wide, fanged and slitted mouth gave it somewhat the appearance of a water-hopper, but no mere water-hopper ever wore an expression so impish. It rubbed its small web-fingered hands together, staring curiously at the girl.

Fawn recognized it as a bandemar, though she had never seen one. Few could claim the distinction, since bandemars transacted their affairs far from the eyes of men. There was some question as to just what manner of life they might be. It was often hinted by the superstitious that they possessed abilities beyond the normal. There were also those who gave testimony to the effect that bandemars were not averse to collecting the foresters' possessions while they slept. Indeed, Fawn thought she had seen small baubles strung inside the seed pod when the little beast emerged.

The bandemar squatted down on its haunches and watched the storm. Fawn, in turn, behaved as though its presence were a matter of indifference to her and went on humming to herself.

At last the storm abated and a few bright rays filtered down through the Narbekian gloom. The bandemar stood peering out the opening, webbed hands on hips, looking very much like a small, petulant old man.

Fawn dressed, leaving the jeweled ornaments sticking in the wall until she was done. When she pulled them out, one dropped to the floor.

The bandemar pounced on it eagerly. The creature examined the small blue stone in the metal setting, turning it round and round. Fawn hesitated momentarily, then reached down and snatched the ornament from its grasp.

The bandemar turned and scuffed casually away to stand at the opening again. If it heard the girl's light laughter, it chose to ignore it.

Fawn stood near the thafa shelter and looked around uncertainly. One section of forest here looked much like another. She might find the right path in minutes or wander in circles for days.

The bandemar, which had followed her out, was seated on a small brown fungus mound that had sprouted during the storm. It stood up and walked away from the girl for a short distance, stopping to glance back at her over its small, bony shoulder with that lone piercing eye. Fawn hesitated only a moment, then shrugged and followed the little being.

The path was ever-winding, and as she continued on without spotting a familiar sign, Fawn's apprehension grew. She pictured herself attacked by lurking hordes of the little demons here, where no one would ever know what had happened to her or to the kluroot.

After a while, however, the girl began to notice several gnarled trees and roots that she thought she had seen before, and she felt slight reassurance. The reservation she still maintained was due to the fact that no one had ever heard of a bandemar helping anyone, and she didn't feel that any form of kinship had been brought about from their brief stay together in the thafa tree.

Several times the bandemar found it necessary to skirt small areas in order to avoid certain dangerous fauna. These were, for the most part, small carnivores of which Fawn had no fear, but on more than one occasion, they narrowly missed confrontation with larger beasts, the ones with contempt—or more likely, simple disregard—for the supremacy of man.

At long last, Fawn stepped onto the well-known trail to her own village. Relieved now to feel herself again on equal footing with her environment, she no longer felt the need for haste. The bandemar had ensured her reaching home with the kluroot before the night came with its slinking dangers, its crawling entrapments, its winging death. She wondered how one explained one's gratitude to a bandemar.

Finding some ripe greatberries, she broke one off and cut the meat into chunks with her small dagger. As she ate she proffered some to the bandemar and it approached slowly, but only stared at her grimly with that one glistening orange eye.

Fawn suddenly felt very drowsy, and although she knew well the perils of sleeping alone and unguarded in the Narbek Forest, she was powerless to resist. Her mind seemed to be drifting off through the trees, losing its grasp on reality.

She awoke moments later to find the bandemar moving away from her in its swaggering stride. She shook her head to clear the cobwebs, brushed a hand through her hair. Then she stopped, abruptly.

Puzzled, she removed the ornament she had felt and looked at it. The blue gem was gone from its setting, although, strangely, the thick bezel was undisturbed. She shrugged, amused at the prospect of her blue stone dangling from a seed pod somewhere in the depths of the forest. But that was not to be its fate.

The bandemar had reached the thicker foliage. It turned, striking an insolent pose and flaunted the gem between two webbed fingers. Then, thrusting out a small green forked tongue, it popped the gem into its empty eye socket.

Other SIGNET Science Fiction Titles You Will Enjoy

☐ **NO TIME LIKE TOMORROW by Brian Aldiss.** Fantastic stories of the future—adventures that soar beyond the barriers of time and space, yet remain perilously close to the boundaries of reality. (#T4605—75¢)

☐ **DOWNWARD TO THE EARTH by Robert Silverberg.** Earthman Edmund Gundersen gambles his body and soul in an alien game where the stakes are immortality. (#T4497—75¢)

☐ **THE DEMOLISHED MAN by Alfred Bester.** A science fiction tale of a ruthless killer who pits his resources against infallible mind-reading detectives. (#T4461—75¢)

☐ **SORCERER'S WORLD by Damien Broderick.** He was primed by the powers of the future for a mighty conquest of the demons of the past . . . and the fate of two worlds hung on the strength of his sword. An adventurous and spellbinding tale of sword and sorcery. (#P4401—60¢)

THE NEW AMERICAN LIBRARY, INC.,
P.O. Box 999, Bergenfield, New Jersey 07621

Please send me the SIGNET BOOKS I have checked above. I am enclosing $_____(check or money order—no currency or C.O.D.'s). Please include the list price plus 15¢ a copy to cover mailing costs.

Name_____

Address_____

City_____State_____Zip Code_____
Allow at least 3 weeks for delivery